Superguide

Complete How-To Manual

By Randall Caba

"Don't step up to the burners without it."

A Neon Press Book
Published by The Neon Press

The Neon Superguide
Complete How-To Manual

A Neon Press Publication

ISBN: 0-9634219-4-8

Book design: The Author
Illustrations: The Author
Technical review: The Author
Book cover design: The Author

Neon art cover photos:
Courtesy of Eric Ehlenberger
and his GlassLight Gallery
(for more information, see Resources)

Limits of Liability and Disclaimer

While every precaution has been taken in the preparation of this book, the author and publisher shall not be liable in the event of incidental or consequential damages in connection with or arising from the contents of this book.

Introduction

If you have never gazed through a telescope at a far away nebula, then perhaps you have seen a picture of one. A nebula is an immense pocket of gas floating in the deep vacuum of space. It emits an array of colored light when its atoms of gas excite to luminous levels by waves of charged particles that race through space.

A magical event occurs when a visible light wave travels in our direction and is not absorbed, reflected or obstructed. If we happen to gaze in the light wave's path, it enters our eye and is focused to strike a single point. When it strikes, its energy is absorbed and converted to an electrical impulse that is sent to our brain. Then depending upon the light wave's energy, we see a particular color.

Such is the way of neon. To mimic the environment in space, a deep vacuum is created within a glass tube. Next, the tube is filled with an inert gas element to precise but very low pressure. Finally, waves of charged particles and energy are beamed through the tube to excite the gas to luminous levels and... we see color.

Then

Some say, the first lit tube arose in 1675 when French astronomer Jean Picard shook a glass tube partially filled with mercury. Friction between the glass wall and the mercury caused static electricity to induce a mercury vapor glow. However, the experiment is most often credited to English scientist Francis Hawksbee (1687-1763) in 1709.

The first glass tube formed into a word was bent in 1744 by Johann Heinrich Winkler (1703-1770). Then in the mid 1800's, Heinrich Geissler (1815-1879) used high voltage and alternating current on evacuated tubes partially filled with gases and vapors to produce light.

Nikola Tesla (1856-1943) used phosphor coated Geissler tubes to spell out the word LIGHT in 1892. However, his tubes did not light long because of impurities within the gas fill and because the electrodes, the devices responsible for delivering charged particles to the gas, were underdeveloped and degenerated quickly.

In 1894, English chemist Sir William Ramsay (1852-1916) and physicist Lord Rayleigh (1842-1919) discovered the inert gas *argon*. Ramsay and Morris W. Travers (1872-1961) then discovered pure *neon* gas in 1898. Inert, unreactive gases lead the way to the first long-lived tubes.

But not until Frenchman Georges Claude (1870-1960) invented and patented for use the long-lived electrode did neon begin to proliferate. In 1910, Claude saw tremendous potential for neon as an indoor and outdoor lighting system. However, his associate, Jacques Fonseque, viewed neon as means for advertising. He sold the first neon sign to a French barbershop in the year 1912.

By 1923, neon found its way to the United States; a famous Los Angeles auto dealer bought two PACKARD signs. The following year Claude began selling neon licenses and franchises throughout the world. Soon there were neon shops in most every major city in the United States.

Soon too, were license and franchise infringements as small shops popped up everywhere to ride the neon wave. Spying, distrust and apprehension permeated the trade while people tried to protect or steal neon secrets. Neon faded from popularity when poorly designed neon signs could no longer compete with the then new and more creative plastic signs of the 1950s.

And Now

But as time marches on, old views and attitudes pass. New tube colors, equipment and technology pour onto the scene and change a trade that has changed little in decades. Yet, the direction the industry takes depends most on the quality of training given its newest members. For the trade to prosper, new members must be welcomed and educated.

Neon glass blowing is a difficult handcraft learned only through patience and rote practice. In fact, some would say that Murphy's Law governs neon manufacturing altogether. So, The Neon Superguide is here to share a methodology for shaping neon tubes and to make common knowledge of a long hidden art. In short, this book is here to educate.

The Neon Superguide is written for the neon craftsman: novice, intermediate and journeyman alike. It covers basic neon tools and equipment but mostly deals with neon glass blowing techniques. For without a shaped glass tube, there is no neon. From creating a pattern, to shaping the tube, lighting and mounting it, it is all here in everyday language as much as possible.

As you work through this book, look at all types of neon: in business windows and shopping malls, on buildings, in artwork and even on cars. Check the progress of your work with that already in the marketplace.

Now, welcome to the world of neon.

Neon is one of few ways that colored light
is shaped by the human hand
into permanent and meaningful forms.

About the Author

Randall Caba worked as Director of Education at The Neon Art and Tube Bending School in Portland, Oregon where he personally trained about two hundred neon craftsmen. He wrote neon course material accepted by the Oregon Department of Education, UAW-Ford, UAW-GM, the Employment Security Division of the Employment Office of the State of Washington and the Accrediting Counsel for Education and Training. For many years, he worked as a neon columnist and feature writer for Sign Builder Illustrated Magazine and made neon signs and art in his home studio. His hobbies include astronomy and writing screenplays.

Contents

CHAPTER

1

The Glassblower's Tools

The glassblower's basic tools are few and simple. Yet, each provides necessary support to the neon craftsman. They consist of the blowhose, glass file, glass pencil, block, tube holder, sandbag and glass gauge.

Blowhose

Molten tubing shrinks in diameter and requires blowing out to maintain proper size. The blowhose allows the glassblower control over air pressure within a tube at a comfortable distance from the heated glass. A cork seals the tube opposite the blowhose.

The blowhose also helps prevent bacteria and other contaminants from being blown directly into the glass tubing from the craftsman's mouth, helping keep the tube interior clean. It also protects the worker from harm due to chipped glass tube ends and potential health hazards related to phosphor tube coatings. Still, many glass craftsman prefer not to use a blowhose. Instead, they blow directly into the end of the glass tube.

A blowhose is three-sixteenth inch or one-quarter inch diameter latex or rubber tubing between four feet and six feet long. The length depends on the craftsman's height and preference. The blowhose is used in combination with a swivel, connector set and mouthpiece. Together, they act as a passage through which the craftsman displaces air into or from a glass tube.

The blowhose is also used to measure the amount of tubing needed to make a section of sign. A permanent mark placed four feet from the blowhose end indicates a typical tube length. By tracing the lines on a neon pattern with the hose, the mark helps determine where a typical glass tube will end during bending.

Swivel

The swivel is made of brass and allows rotation of the glass tube without kinking or twisting the blowhose. One side of the swivel is inserted into the end of the blowhose opposite the mouthpiece. The other is inserted into a connector that connects the blowhose to the glass tube. Swivels are made angled about thirty to ninety-degrees to better their use.

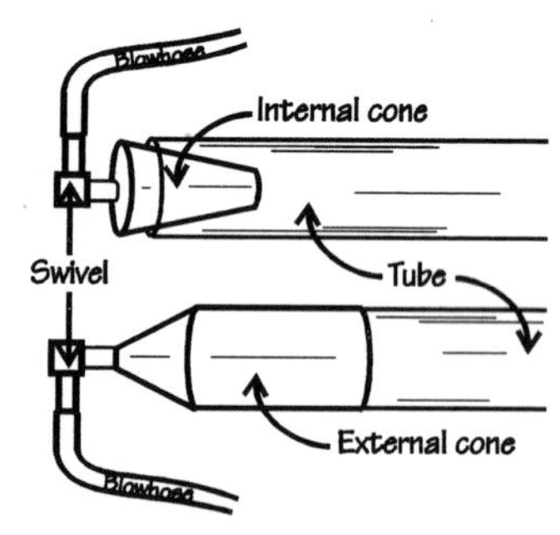

Figure 1-1 Connectors and swivels

Connectors

Connectors consist of internal and external hollow cones. The large end of the internal cone plugs onto the swivel. The tapered end fits inside a glass tube to help form an air tight seal. Internal cones are made of rubber.

The external, hollow cone is made of vinyl in different sizes. It fits over the outside of glass tubing. The external cone often is used on phosphor coated glass tubes because it does not loosen phosphors adhered inside.

Mouthpiece

The mouthpiece is a small glass tube, five or six millimeters in diameter, made to rest inside the mouth. The mouthpiece connects the craftsman to the rest of the blowhose apparatus. See Figure 1-4.

Glass File and Pencil

A metal file is used to cut glass tubing. Ordinarily, it is a double-cut mill-bastard type, six to eight inches long. Most craftsmen develop a particular cutting style to separate tubing. These and other cutting methods are described and illustrated in detail in Chapter Three.

A mark is made on a glass tube so the craftsman knows where to perform a particular action, such as a bend or cut. Since most pencils do not mark on glass tubing at all, a special glass pencil is used to make this mark. It is a pencil that will mark on glass tubing and will not burn off in a flame. Stabilos®, grease pencils, chalk and even soap stone are examples of products used to mark glass tubes.

Blocks and Tube Holders

Blocks are used to straighten molten, welded tubes, press softened bent tubing flat and provide a consistent elevation for three dimensional bends. Most blocks are made of wood covered with a heat resistant fabric. This fabric is made up of non-asbestos material, fiberglass and silicone, and currently sells under the name Nonsbestos® or Transbestos®.

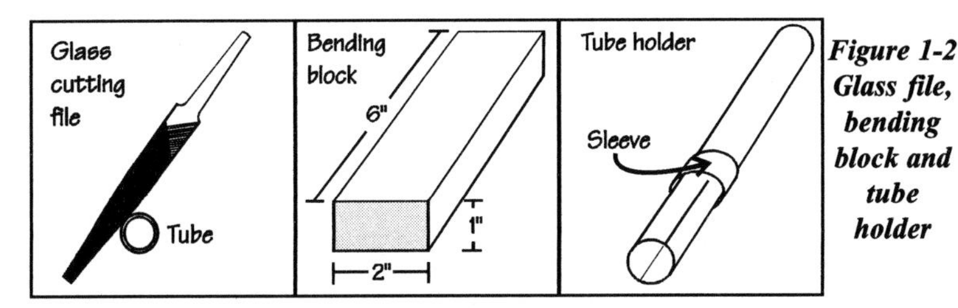

Figure 1-2 Glass file, bending block and tube holder

Block size is determined by worker preference and job type. A one inch by two inch by six inch block works well with twelve millimeter to fifteen millimeter diameter tubes. Often, a block less than one inch in height is used when working with smaller diameter tubes.

The tube holder is used to extend short lengths of tubing and to hold electrodes while welding and bending. They are six inch to twelve inch long tubes made of brass, split about one-third their length. A sliding collar or sleeve tightens the holder around an inserted tube. Instead of using a tube holder, some craftsmen simply weld temporarily a piece of scrap tubing onto a short tube to act as an extension.

Sandbag

A sandbag is a small bag made of fabric or other material filled with sand. It is used to hold still one section of tubing while it is tubulated or to hold still another section while being welded. Other kinds of weight are used too, like lead bars and sand filled cans, but a sandbag distributes its weight evenly across bent glass tubing lessening strain points and chance for breakage.

Glass Gauge

The glass gauge measures the glass tube diameter in millimeters. Made of thin gauge metal, it is slotted in v-shape so a tube inserted into the slot stops at a given numbered point revealing the tube diameter.

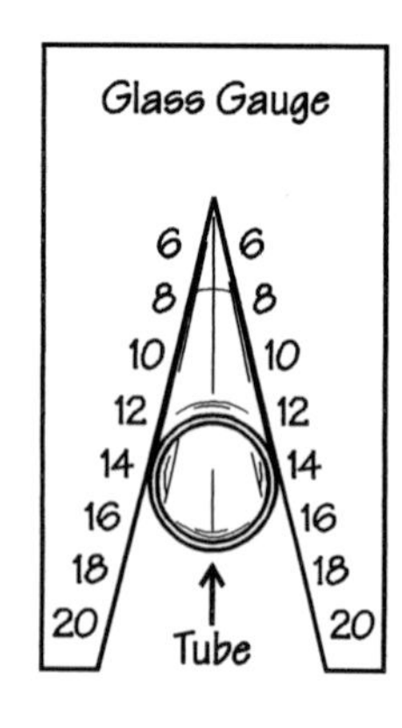

Figure 1-3 Glass gauge

Exercises

Making a Mouthpiece

To make a mouthpiece, heat until soft the end of five or six millimeter diameter glass tubing. Form a flare by gently inserting into the softened tube end a cone shaped object, like a fillips screw driver. Heat the flare to molten and press straight down onto a flat surface to create a thick, flat ridge. The ridge helps hold the mouthpiece in the mouth usually behind a tooth. Let the piece cool completely before inserting into your mouth.

One inch to two inches from the ridge, heat the tube until it bends about seventy to ninety-degrees. Allow the glass to cool completely. Now, cut the tube one or two inches from the seventy degree bend. Finally, insert the cut end roughly one-half inch into a blowhose.

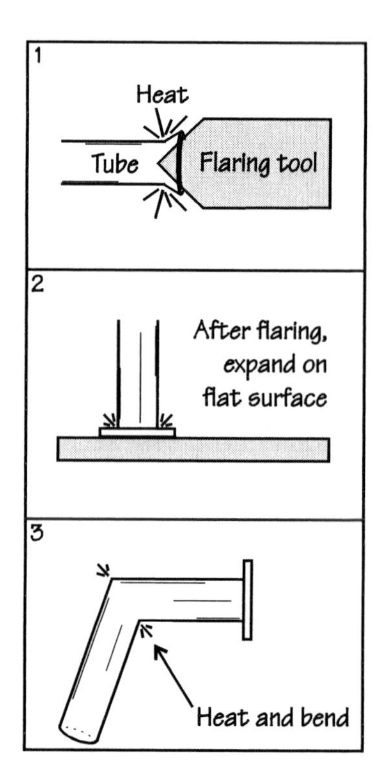

Figure 1-4 One way to make a mouthpiece

Another way to form the flare is to rotate the molten tube end against the thin end of a file. Repeatedly heat the flare then rotate against the file at increasing angles. This forms a greater flare each time the tube and file meet. Before cooling, heat the flare near molten to remove any strain within the glass, strain created as the cool metal file rapidly pulled heat from the molten tube. Strain within a glass tube usually results in cracks or breaks.

Tips and Hints

1. Before doing any glasswork, get an eye exam. Good eye-hand coordination is necessary to safely learn neon glass bending. Wear safety glasses or goggles too if you prefer.
2. Hang the blowhose vertically overnight. This allows unwanted moisture to drain. Once your mouth becomes use to the mouthpiece, salivation will decrease and so will moisture problems.
3. Use multiple blowhoses when mass-producing the same sign. Switching a single blowhose from tube to tube takes time and causes needless wear on the connector set.
4. The blowhose weakens overtime so, weekly check for leaks near the swivel and mouthpiece. Cut away any discolored or leaking hose. Replace with new hose every few or so months.
5. Sometimes the blowhose ends up resting on molten glass. Cut away the damaged section and splice the remaining two pieces together with a short piece of five millimeter glass tubing.
6. Keep your tongue away from the end of the mouthpiece while heating glass tubing in a flame. This effectively seals the tube leaving hot, expanding air with nowhere to displace. The expanding air causes the molten glass to swell into undesirable shapes.
7. Before working a sealed tube, blow into the blowhose just before entering a fire to ensure an air seal.
8. If a brass tube holder is stuck on a tube or electrode, gently warm it well over the top of a flame. This causes the holder to expand making it easy to remove. Take care not to burn your fingers on the tube, electrode or tube holder.
9. To weld a tubulated electrode using a tube holder, pass only the blowhose through the tube holder's opposite end. Then connect the hose to the tubulation. Or, temporarily seal the electrode tubulation by inserting a short pipe cleaner. Then attach the blowhose to the tube that the electrode is to be attached.

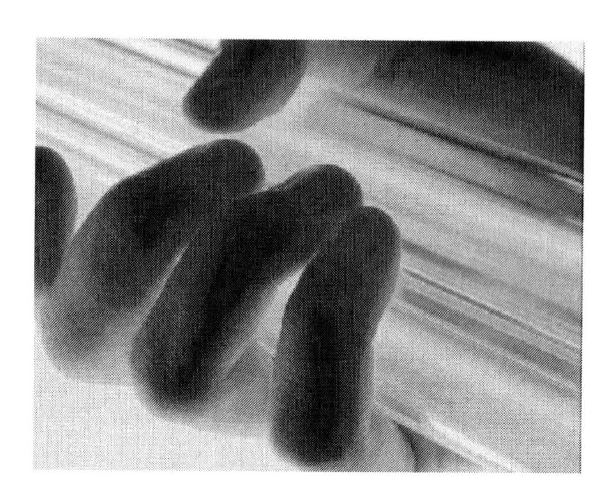

Figure 1-6
For the most part neon remains a true handcraft
(www.freeimages.co.uk)

CHAPTER

2

Shop Equipment

Inefficient equipment can limit the ability of even a talented neon craftsman. And improper gas or air supply can limit the function of good glass bending equipment. Therefore, it is important to purchase equipment designed for the neon trade. The modern neon shop is available for sale as a kit with all of the necessary parts matched to operate efficiently.

Glass Bending Plant

All glass bending plants should include the following: A table designed for glass bending. An air pump capable of delivering a steady flow of air at low pressure. A fuel supply such as natural gas or propane to operate the burners. An air/gas manifold and mixers for adjusting air and gas flow to the burners. A crossfire or cannon fire, a handtorch and ribbon burner to heat the glass.

Bending Table

The glass bending table should be level and comfortable to the glass worker. Too low or too high a table affects the craftsman's speed and quality of work. Most bending tables are thirty-two to forty inches high with built-in shelving for glass, equipment and tool storage. Usually, the work surface is four foot by eight foot or larger, ideal for working on most sign types.

The table surface must be level and capable of withstanding high temperature, up to twelve hundred degrees Fahrenheit. A common table surface is three sixteenths to one-quarter inch smooth plywood. It is attached to a sturdy wood frame or off-the-shelf, metal frame kit found in department or home improvement stores.

Heat resistant sheetrock or gypsum board is frequently laid atop the plywood. The sheetrock provides a flat surface with helpful heat resistant properties that absorb heat then reflect it back at the molten glass slowing cooling. This helps reduce strain from developing within the glass work. A final covering with a non-asbestos, silicone and fiberglass fabric, completes the bending surface. This nonflammable material is available from local sign supply distributors.

Figure 2-1 Typical worktable construction

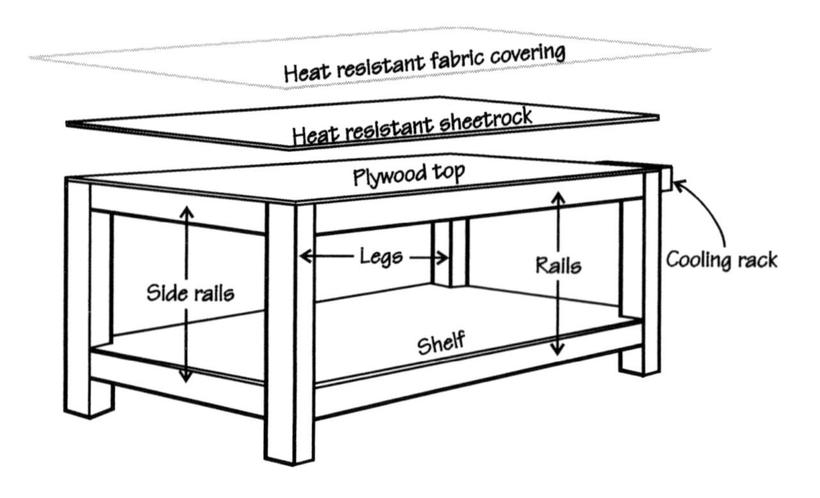

A cooling rack is sometimes attached to the bending table or near it. After a bend is made and has cooled somewhat, the tube is stood in the rack while other work continues. The additional cooling time helps reduce chance of strain developing in the bend. A cooling rack is made by drilling several one-half inch to three-quarter inch holes about three inches deep in a four-by-four piece of wood. The cooling tubes are stood in the holes.

Air Supply or Blower

The air supply, blower or air pump as it is called, must be designed for continuous use. A leaf blower delivers usable air pressure and volume for a one-man shop, but ordinarily burns out in short order. A typical neon shop blower delivers air at about forty cubic feet per minute and at pressure of two to three pounds per square inch. Large shops or small shops expecting to expand need a larger blower proportional to their size or expected size.

Figure 2-2
Regenerative air blower
(Daco Neon Equipment)

An inexpensive blower or improperly aligned blower motor can cause oscillating air surges requiring use of a surge tank. Typically, a surge tank is one to five gallons in capacity. Through it, surging air is buffered by the container expanse before the air exits to the burners. A relief valve found on most blowers helps buffer air surges too.

Fuel Supply

Fuel is needed to operate the burners. Natural gas, provided by underground piping, or propane stored in pressurized cylinders, are the most commonly used fuels. It is necessary to match the fuel with the burner. Natural gas burners are engineered slightly different from propane burners and operate properly only with natural gas. Propane burners operate best with propane fuel but do work well with natural gas. A pressure-reducing regulator is required when using propane since it is stored under high pressure. As with any fuel, observe all safety requirements.

Air/Gas Manifold

The air/gas manifold consists of two pipes, one to two inches in diameter each. Air flows through one pipe and natural gas or propane through the other. Valves attached to the pipes are used to make final burner adjustment. An air valve is larger than a gas valve since more air is needed than gas to support a flame. Large burners, like the ribbon burner, require bigger valves than small burners because they consume more air and gas. Systems that are more expensive use multi-turn needle valves that offer finer gas flow adjustment than non-regulating valves like common water valves. Some compact systems integrate both the blower and air/gas manifold.

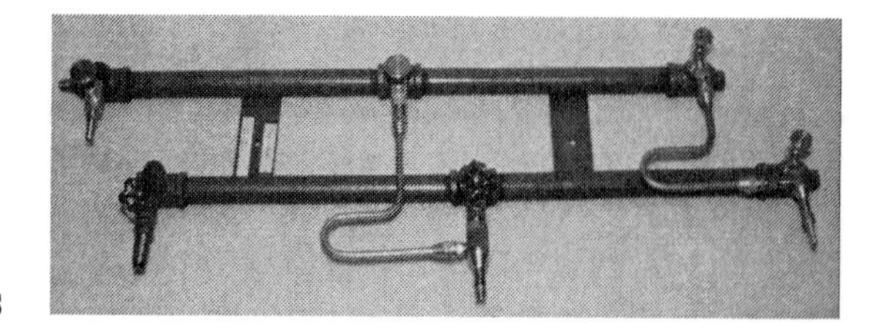

Figure 2-3 Air/gas manifold system (Daco Neon Equipment)

Air/Gas Mixers

Tubing made from vinyl or rubber connects the air/gas manifold valves to a mixer. Here air and gas are blended before entering the burner. Mixer styles range from a simple T-connector to the more sophisticated venturi mixer. The ribbon burner, if equipped with an economizer, needs no T- or venturi mixer as the economizer mixes both air and gas fuel.

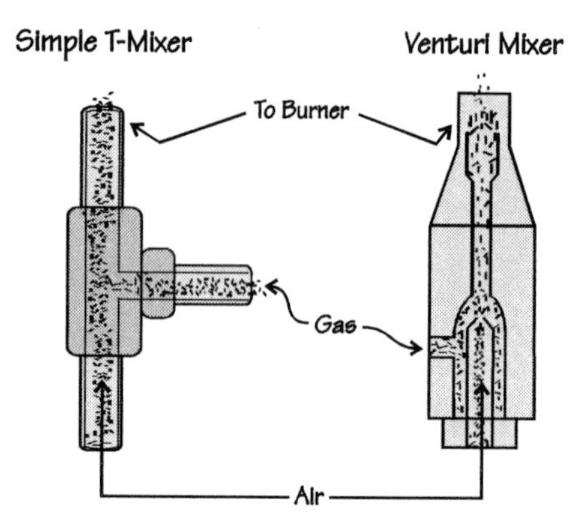

Figure 2-4 Various air/gas mixer function

General Burner Adjustment

The following flow chart aids in the initial adjustment of any torch. If after this initial adjustment, the flame is wispy and cool, more air and probably more gas is needed. If the flame is hot but blows out occasionally, less air and possibly less gas is required. Proper burner adjustment takes practice. The chart offers a good starting point for regulating any burner type used in neon manufacturing. See Figure 2-5.

Crossfire

The function of the crossfire is what its name implies, to set up a cross fire of flame. Crossfires consist of a total of ten, twelve, or fourteen "finger" burners. They are divided equally between two manifolds. The individual burners are angled to focus the flames at one point. A crossfire with more fingers obviously provides more heat. Still, some tubebenders mount a helper fire beneath the crossfire fingers. The helper fire simply increases the tube-heating rate.

The crossfire is used to make welds, basic bends and tubulations. On some burners, one finger burner swings away to aid tubulating. The intensely focused flame of the crossfire is especially helpful when making small letters or close bends.

Figure 2-5 Burner adjustment flow chart

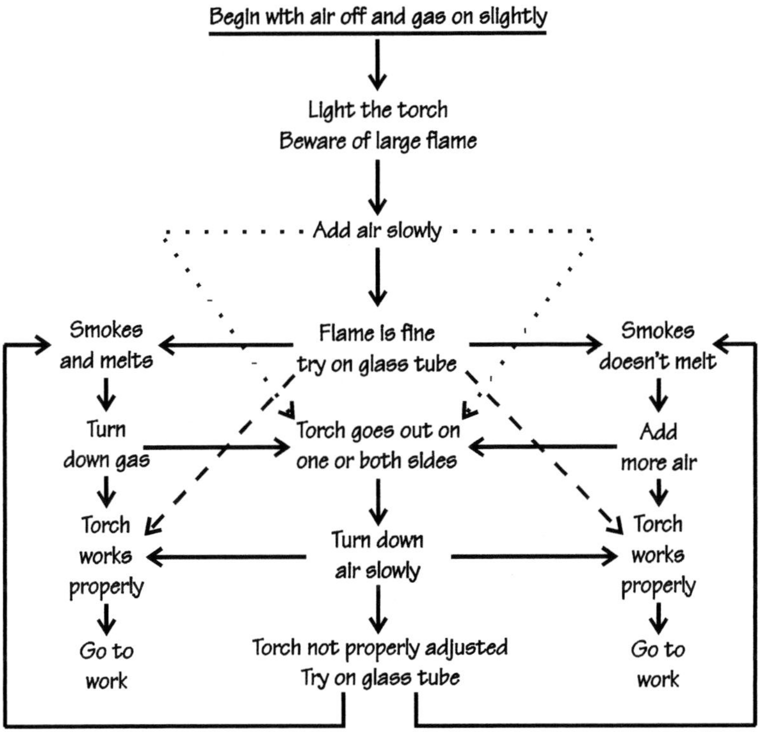

Cannon Fire

The typical cannon fire is made of two large circular burners or heads. Each burner provides flame through many small orifices. Instead of creating a point of flame, the burners focus flame over a circular area. This large area of flame helps to evenly heat around a glass tube. Cannon burners often are used to bend large diameter tubes because they heat tubing faster than crossfires. Experienced glassworkers sometimes use helper fires with cannon burners too.

Handtorch

The handtorch is used for welding tubes and making tubulations. It uses two round or fishtail shaped brass burners. The handtorch makes welding unwieldy tubes easier since the flame is brought to the tube. Still, many tubebenders prefer welding even unwieldy tubes in cross or cannon fires.

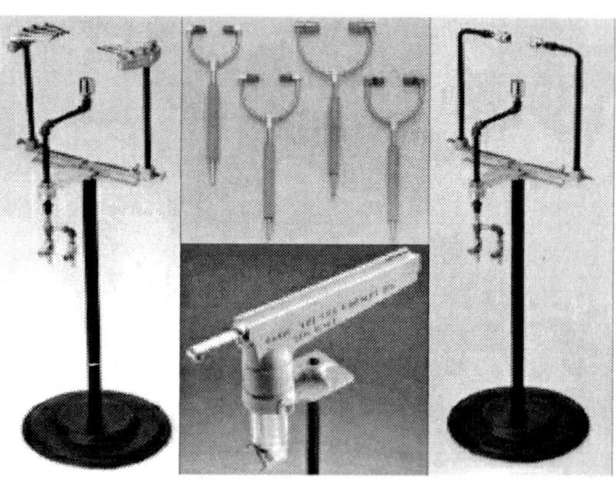

Figure 2-6
Clockwise: crossfire, handtorch, cannon fire, ribbon burner (Transco)

Handtorches are available in various sizes. Smaller handtorches are usually used to weld small tubes, five through twelve millimeter in diameter. Tubes larger than twelve millimeter often are welded with a bigger handtorch, since large tubes require more heat to soften the glass.

A few shops sport the jeweler's torch. It uses a single, oxygen fed burner instead of the conventional two-burner arrangement like the handtorch. The single tip, oxygen boosted flame produces high heat that speeds up any handtorch job.

Ribbon Burner

The ribbon burner is used to form sweeping curves, circles and script style lettering. It uses a long narrow head to produce a ribbon of flame. Ordinarily, gas and air are supplied separately to an adjustable mixing chamber called the economizer where the ribbon burner sits. The economizer allows the operator quick control over flame temperature between idle and roaring.

Ribbon fires are commonly offered in three sizes: the six inch, sixteen inch and the twenty-four inch. The most common ribbon burner is the sixteen inch. It produces a flame about one inch wide and up to sixteen inches in length. A flat metal strip slides across the burner head to adjust flame length.

Twenty-four inch ribbons use two, twelve inch sliders to control the flame length. Rather than opening from one end, like the six and sixteen inch, the twenty-four opens from the center. Regardless of size, most ribbon burners generate less heat at the ends of the flame than the middle. Heating an inch or two beyond the desired molten tube length compensates for this.

Figure 2-7
1950's craftsman working in a ribbon burner

Bombarding and Pumping Equipment

Internal bombarding is an electrical heating process that helps to purify the inside of the finished tube. Proper bombarding requires a vacuum pump to lower air pressure within the tube and a high voltage transformer to heat the impurities trapped inside. A regulator is used to control the electric current through the tube. A manifold system allows the operator control over vacuum and gassing procedures. Respectively, this equipment is called the vacuum pump, the bombarding transformer or bombarder, the choke coil or choke and the pumping manifold. Another common tube processing accessory is the spark coil tester or Tesla coil used to locate leaks.

Vacuum Pump

A vacuum pump is used to "process" neon tubes. It helps remove heated, vaporized impurities that otherwise left within a tube would cause problems like shortened tube life, dimming, discoloration or mercury stains.

The typical vacuum pump used to process neon tubes is a two-stage design capable of creating and maintaining an ultimate pressure of five microns or less. A single stage pump does not produce sufficient vacuum for effective tube processing.

Figure 2-8 Direct and belt drive two-stage vacuum pumps (Daco)

A typical small, two-stage vacuum pump is capable of displacing about thirty liters of air per minute (L/min), around one cubic foot per minute (cfm) and is often used in small or low production shops. A medium pump moves about seventy-five to two hundred L/min. And a large vacuum pump displaces air at three hundred to more than one thousand L/min. High production shops processing several tubes simultaneously use a medium to large pump. Others use a mechanical pump for initial "rough" pumping and a second mechanical pump for "fine" pumping or add a diffusion pump for extreme pumping.

Bombarder and Choke

The bombarder is a high voltage-electric transformer used to heat the tube during tube processing. It ranges in size from five Kva to twenty Kva and more. Kva is the abbreviation for kilo-volt-amperes. The Kva rating is determined by multiplying the primary voltage (usually two hundred and twenty volts) by the primary current (measured in amperes) and dividing by one thousand. Most neon shops use ten Kva to fifteen Kva rated bombarding transformers.

The bombarder is wired to an electrical choke that regulates power generated by the bombarder. Many types of choke exist but each is used to regulate secondary current at the sign during tube processing. Current control is necessary to heat safely both the tube and electrodes.

Pumping Manifold

The typical pumping manifold is a glass apparatus made of a bank of stopcocks. It allows the operator control of many factors within the tube during processing. These factors include degree of vacuum, introduction and measurement of inert gases and means of leak testing.

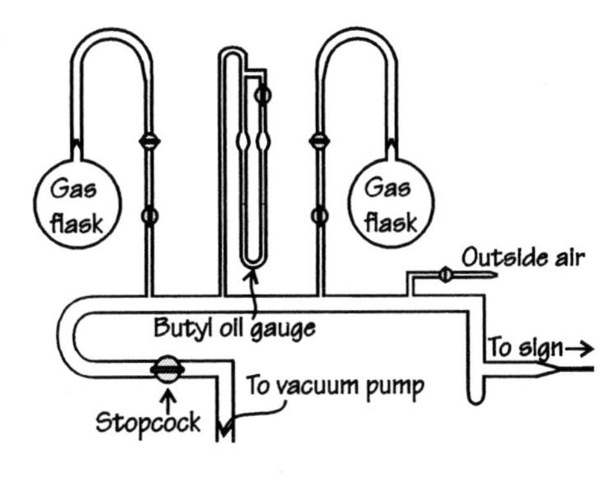

Figure 2-9 Schematic of a typical glass manifold

Spark Coil and Color Tester

The spark coil is a high voltage, high frequency generator capable of throwing an electrical ground-seeking spark. It helps the operator to locate an air leak within a completed, evacuated tube and determine the color of coated tubes.

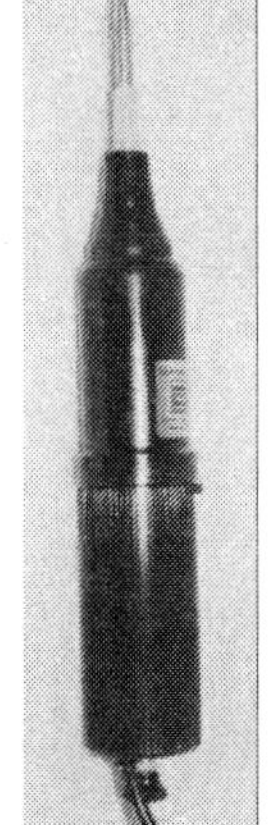

Figure 2-10 Spark coil
(Daco Neon Equipment)

The spark coil generates an electric spark that exposes a hole in a tube by lighting it and sticking to it. For this test, the tube must be under vacuum since the spark seeks electrical ground through the vacuum.

Most unlit, coated tubes are white and when unlabeled the tube color is nearly impossible to determine. A trick used to discover tube color is to lay a file or other metal object over the tube end. By generating a spark with the spark coil inside the tube, under the metal object, part of the coating will light. This allows reasonable determination of tube color. However, commercial ultraviolet lamps, used much like a flashlight, are better suited for coated tube color testing. Simply shine the tester light inside a coated tube and the phosphor coating lights exposing its true color.

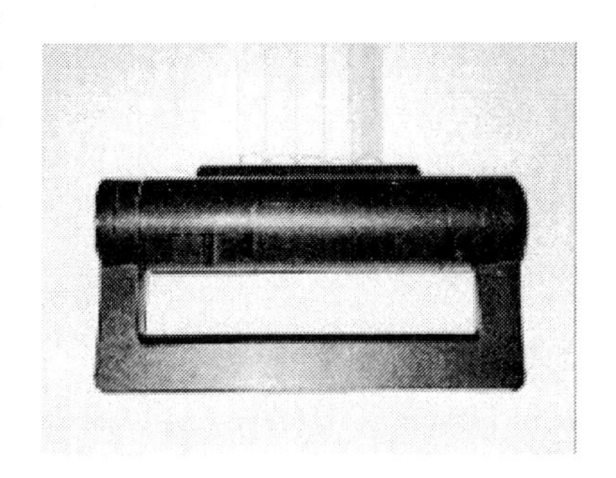

Figure 2-11 Ultraviolet coated-tube color tester

Tips for Setting Up Shop

1. Shop equipment and layout

a. Buy equipment designed for the industry. Start-up costs are relatively low compared to other business and cutting corners now may cost more later. Neon shop equipment is often offered as a matched kit.

b. Mount burner adjusting valves to the burners or to the bending table to make burner adjustment convenient. Route burner hoses out of the workplace, under or around tables or under a raised floor.

c. Leave room on all sides of burners for an unencumbered work space.

d. Keep glass and electrode supplies nearby.

e. Store patterns systematically, perhaps alphabetically.

2. Comfort

a. Make work tables the proper size for type of glass work: build a bending table four by eight feet, make processing and burn-in tables three feet by ten feet or use three by ten foot shelves for burn-in (all sizes minimum).

b. Keep noise levels under control. If necessary, mount the air pump outdoors under cover or in another room and mount the vacuum pump in a cabinet.

c. Use adequate ventilation to remove heat and vapors from burners.

d. Place antifatigue mats at all work stations.

e. Use a radio or stereo system to make work pass more enjoyably.

3. Safety

a. Use a bombarder warning light to show when it is active.

b. Designate with a sign both gas and bombarder shutoff.

c. Post fire extinguishers about the shop according to regulation.

d. Control mercury spills with a spill kit found at science supply stores.

e. Keep a first aid kit handy for cuts, burns and other injuries.

f. Observe all equipment installation and operating instructions.

Cleaning Burners

Eventually, all burners require cleaning to operate efficiently. Clean brass parts with Muriatic acid. Soak the parts in the acid for about a minute or less—the acid can damage metal parts if left in contact too long. Immediately, rinse the part with sufficient water to insure all acid is washed away. Keep in mind, Muriatic acid is very strong and can be hazardous when misused. Safe use and disposal is essential. Dry the part thoroughly then finish cleaning burner orifices with a welder's tip cleaner or other brush.

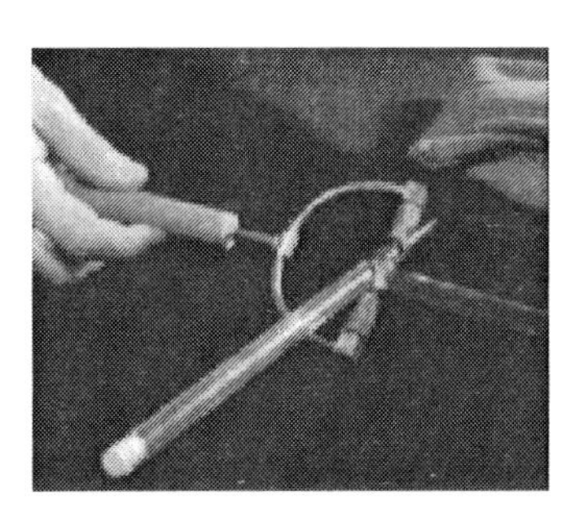

Figure 2-12 Tubulating with a handtorch (Photo Design)

Figure 2-13 Bending in a ribbon burner (Photo Design)

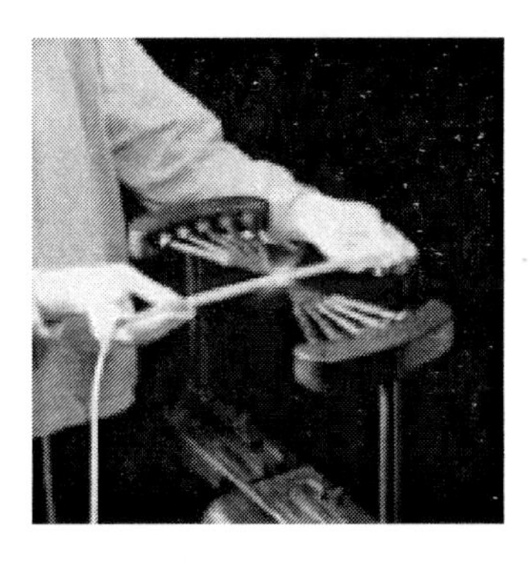

Figure 2-14 Welding in a crossfire (Photo Design)

Figure 2-15 Bombarding also called tube processing (Photo Design)

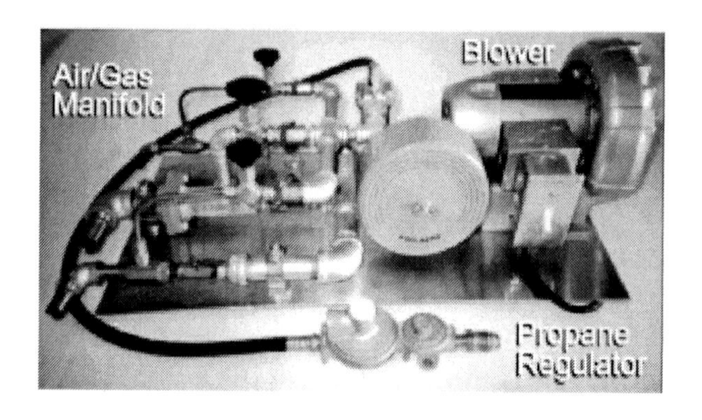

Figure 2-16
Portable combination air blower,
air/gas manifold and gas regulator

CHAPTER

3

Cutting Glass Tubing

For the neon craftsman, cutting glass tubing is a common task. Most use a flat, double-cut file to etch the tube surface—the etch strains the glass. Pulling, tapping or otherwise coercing the glass apart completes the cut. The goal is to create a smooth, even end cut to ease welding.

Using the File

Long lengths of tubing, more than two feet long, are easy to separate. Hold the file at a forty-five degree angle to the tube. Firmly pull the file across the tube to create the desired score. A quick pull on the tube in opposite directions cleanly snaps the tubing apart. If the tube does not separate on the first try, a second scoring is necessary. An experienced craftsman can consistently cut long lengths of tubing in this fashion.

Short lengths are more difficult to cut and require extra effort and care to achieve good results. In these instances, the file is used with a sawing motion using most of the file length. The tube is rotated under the file to form an etch about one-half way around. Eventually, a light tap with a file edge separates the tube. Consistently making a straight score of the correct depth requires practice.

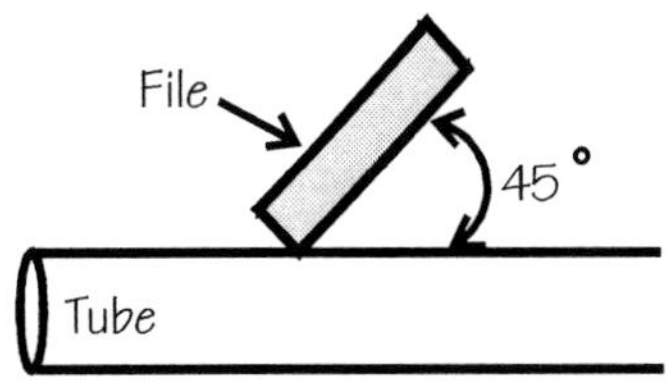

Figure 3-1 Correct file angle

Excessive force or repeated taps may produce unsatisfactory results. Most the magic of cutting lies in the pressure exerted on the file, about two to three pounds, the motion applied and experience.

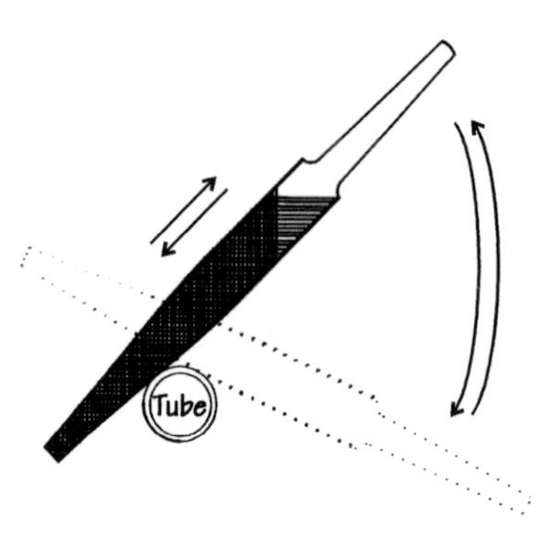

Figure 3-2
Scoring motion

On extremely short lengths of tubing or when the cut is very near a bend or weld, continued scoring separates the tube best. Move the file with saw like motion applying downward pressure. Rotate the tube to form a score about one-half way around. Repeat this motion until the tube separates cleanly.

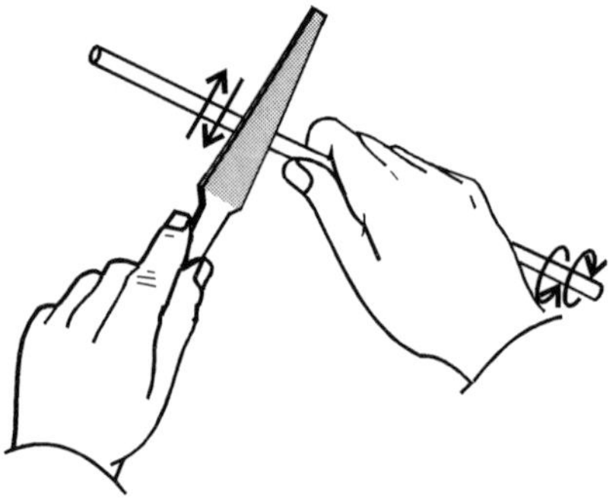

Figure 3-3 Cutting glass tubing

Sharpening the File

The file is dull and requires sharpening when it slips across the tube surface as though on ice or if it chips the glass. Using a dull file to cut results in uneven tube ends. You can sharpen a file by drawing the file edge, not face, flat across a rotating grinding stone. Do not tip the file edge into the stone however as this will bevel the teeth and dull it.

Other Cutting Methods

Tungsten-carbide cutters also are used to cut glass tubing though they are not widely used in the United States. Used more like a glass knife, a very thin scratch is made in the glass tube. Then a quick pull with a slight outward force separates the tubing. Like most skills, good results come with experience.

A third tool used for cutting tubing is the electric cutter. A circular wire is wrapped around the tube where the cut is to be made. Applied electricity heats the wire to a dull red color. The heat is applied for several seconds then quickly removed. The heated glass is quickly dabbed with a damp rag, swab or finger. The expansion then sudden contraction of glass molecules creates a strain that parts the tube. Some craftsmen etch the glass before applying the electric cutter.

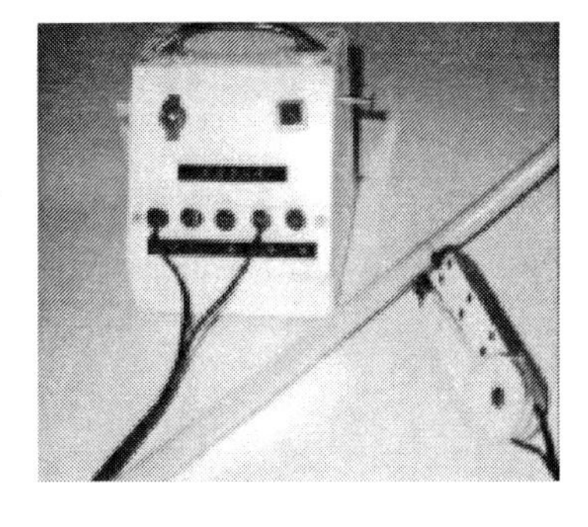

Figure 3-4 The electric cutter

Tips and Hints

1. Hold onto the important part of the letter or design and cut the unimportant piece free. This reduces risk of dropping and breaking the usable part of the glass tube.
2. On an uneven cut, turn the tube so the excess glass is positioned on top. Then cut down through the uneven portion making the end flush.
3. When a cork gets stuck inside a tube, cut the tube end halfway down the cork until it separates. Then simply push the cork from the remaining small section of tubing.
4. Periodically during manufacture, look in a tube for debris. Glass particles from cutting, pieces of blowhose connector and cork, sometimes find their way into a tube. During processing, the tube is heated enough that this debris burns inside the tube and causes problems.
5. Cutting a tube with a file on a table damages the tabletop over time. So, cut the tubing on a sign pattern or on an unused corner of the table. This helps keep the table surface from undue damage and lessens maintenance.

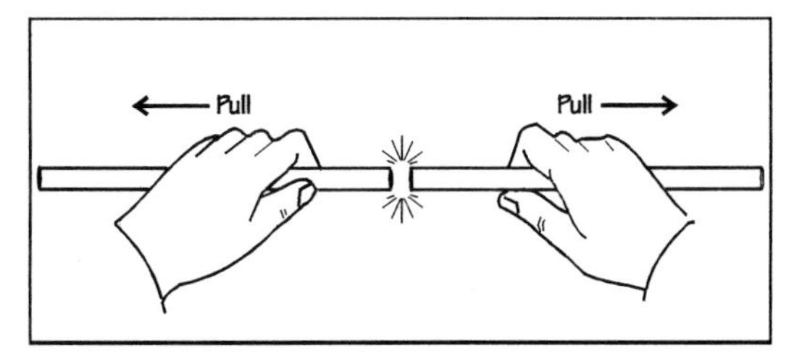

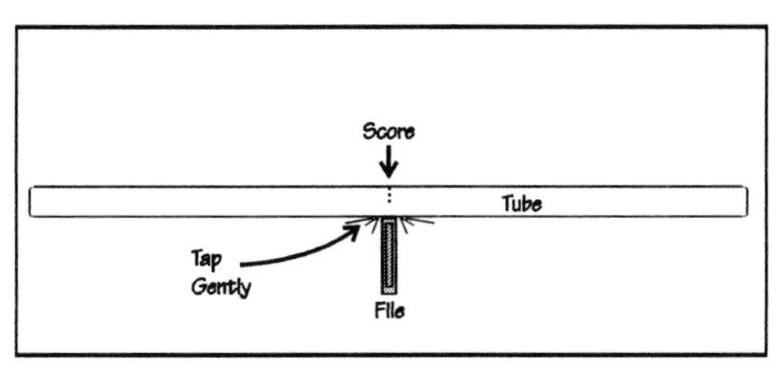

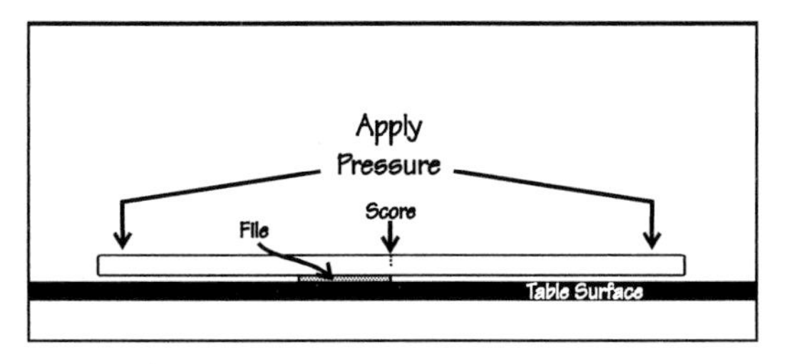

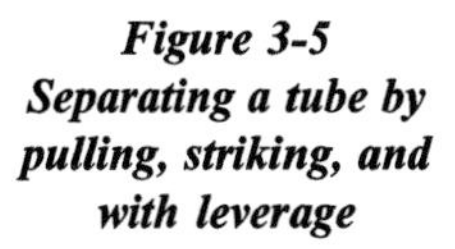

Figure 3-5 Separating a tube by pulling, striking, and with leverage

CHAPTER

4

Glass Properties, Welding and Tubulating

Before actually putting the glass to flame, it is important to understand the effects heating and cooling have on glass tubing. All types of glass have several measurable properties including strength, viscosity, and rate of expansion, softening point, working temperature, annealing point and strain point. These and many other factors are considered during glass tube fabrication. The latter five concern the neon glass worker since these effect glass working. For the most part, they make up the *working personality* of the glass tube.

Glass Working Properties and Annealing

The softening point of a glass tube is an important consideration. Conventional neon tube bending equipment works only with soft glass, lead glass and soda glass. Hard glass tubes, like borosilicate, require higher temperature flame and often add oxygen to the fuel to increase flame temperature.

Glass annealing temperature is the temperature glass is heated to remove strains. Although neon tubing is virtually strain free when purchased, strains can develop during heating and cooling. Developing a sense of when molten glass is nearing the annealing point is essential to produce nearly strain free work.

Within this text, *table annealing* is referred to now and again though it is not proper annealing. Proper annealing is heating the finished glasswork to annealing temperature, or slightly above, then precisely controlling the cooling rate to the strain point. The cooling rate for proper annealing is determined by the thickness of the glass and its chemical composition.

Common neon tubing is made of lead glass, composed mostly of lead oxide and silica, and is inexpensive to manufacture. The lead oxide and silica mixture lowers both glass softening and working temperature offering reasonable time to work the molten glass. It also creates a kind of glass that expands and contracts substantially with heat.

The property of expansion is measured numerically as a coefficient of expansion or expansion rate. The larger the expansion rate the greater chance strain might develop if the glass is not worked properly. Large differences in coefficients of expansion mean two types of glass will not seal together, like lead glass and borosilicate.

Soda-Lime glass is also used to make neon signs but is not as common as lead glass. Also called classic or exotic glass, soda-lime tubes are more difficult to work and require a little hotter flame. Classic tubes are much more expensive than lead glass tubes but offer an array of rich colors. They are available both coated and uncoated to offer more colors.

Figure 4-1 Glass properties

Glass Characteristics
(temperatures are approximate in degrees Fahrenheit)

Glass Type	Softening Point Temperature	Working Point Temperature	Annealing Point Temperature	Strain Point Temperature	Expansion Rate
Clear Lead	1166	1805	815	745	90
Soda-Lime	1283	1855	957	883	92
Borosilicate	1392	2095	973	903	32

Welding or Splicing

Welding, also called splicing, is joining or sealing two tubes together by heat. It is a task best performed in a crossfire, cannon fire or with a handtorch though some attempt this in a ribbon burner too.

It is important to be still and balanced during welding. So, position feet shoulder width apart with hands palms up. Hold elbows lightly against the ribs with shoulders relaxed.

To make a weld, connect a blowhose to one tube end and seal another tube end with a cork. This is so you can work the glass with air once the tubes are joined. In a crossor cannon fire, balance the tubes across the middle of all four fingers so rolling the tube from thumb to fingertip is easy. Rolling is slow and controlled, not frantic. Heat the tube ends to molten and gently touch them together. Roll the tube and visually inspect to assure proper alignment. Heat the seam until the tube diameter shrinks then work the tube outside the flame, above or below. Do this by gently sucking in then blowing out. Do not use lung force.

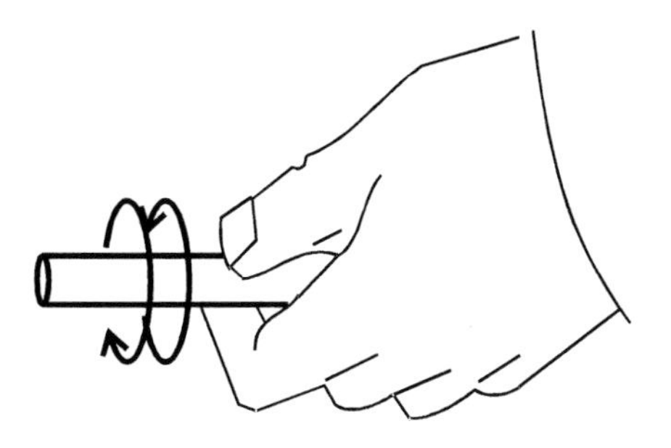

Figure 4-2 Rolling a tube while heating

While working the weld, check that the tube is straight by turning the glass. A good routine is to suck-blow-turn, then suck-blow-turn again before returning to the fire. This heating then working is done repeatedly until the weld is complete, the tube sealed and smooth in appearance. A final blow into the tube returns its original diameter.

With the seam still molten, lower the tube to the table. Quickly straighten by pressing the tube once between two blocks, excessive use of blocks may cause strain. Some craftsmen roll the tube across the table to smooth it before straightening. The tube must be very molten when sat down then rolled rapidly to maintain even heat. A little air pressure helps maintain diameter.

Next, allow the tube to table anneal. Let it cool slowly and evenly from softening point to ridged state without being moved. Ordinarily, this takes about twenty to sixty seconds depending on tube diameter and glass type. Large tubes heat and cool more slowly than small tubes due to greater mass. However, be aware the tube remains extremely, sometimes dangerously hot to the touch for three to four minutes.

After the tube has cooled, inspect the seam. It should feel smooth and produce no *lens effect.* A lens effect indicates stretching or thinning of the glass wall. Excessive gathering appears as wall thickening that can cool unevenly causing strain.

There are many ways to weld. Once a feel for working glass develops, other techniques may be used. When *jiggle* or *twist* welding, the tube can remain in the flame allowing the heat to make the weld.

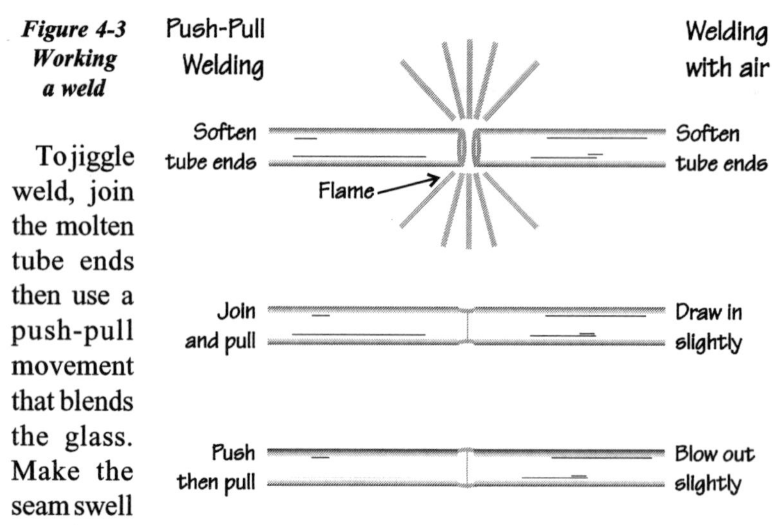

Figure 4-3 Working a weld

To jiggle weld, join the molten tube ends then use a push-pull movement that blends the glass. Make the seam swell a millimeter or two when pushing then pull the tube returning the seam to near original diameter. Perform this jiggling motion several times to blend the glass completely.

To twist weld, slightly rotate each tube in opposite directions until the seam blends. Some craftsman use combinations of these techniques to form a weld.

Handtorch Welding

Welding large or awkwardly bent tubes is more comfortable with a handtorch. Position one tube so the handtorch turns freely where it is to be welded. Set this point off a table edge or raise it above the table on a block. Use a weight, sandbag or lead bar, to hold this unit steady.

Balance the other tube or piece in one hand for easy manipulation during welding. As much as possible, align the torch handle parallel to the tube and rotate the flame about it rhythmically, one-quarter turn. This motion evenly heats the tube ends.

Use a bumping action if the torch heats the tube too slowly. Bumping is moving one torch head close to the tube briefly then moving the other in close. One flame is left nearer the splice only a fraction of a second before moving the opposite flame for a bump. This motion aids heating the tube faster. After bumping each flame once or twice, rotate the torch one-quarter turn and bump again. Count if it helps bumping the flames on each count: two, three, four, rotate, two, three, four, rotate, etcetera until the glass softens.

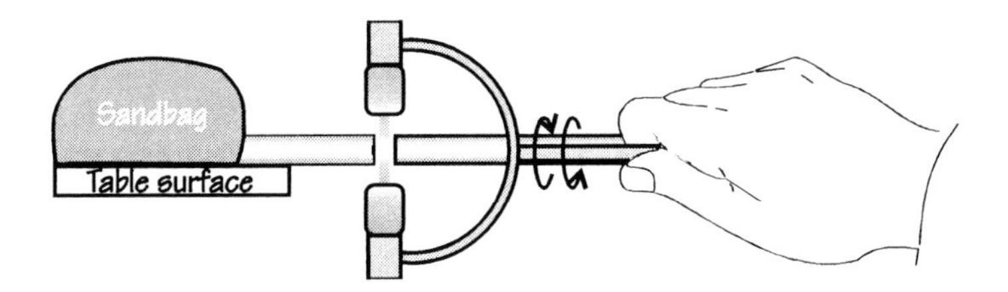

Figure 4-4 Handtorch welding

If the glass blackens, the flame is too rich-high in gas-or is being brought too close to the weld. This darkening is the metal lead chemically reduced from the glass lead oxide. Known as "smoked" glass; it often causes a leak or weakens the tube.

If an obvious hole develops during welding, bend the tube in the direction of the hole during heating. This motion joins the glass, sealing the hole. Once sealed, slowly straighten the tube and work the seam until the weld is complete.

Testing a Weld

To test a weld for strains, carefully pass it through a flame after cooling. A bad weld will crack or shatter. A good weld can withstand being held directly in the fire until molten without mishap. Or it can be used in bends without kinking or changing diameter—this would indicate glass wall thickening or thinning within the seam.

Welding Coated and Classic Tubes

Welding coated tubing is best done in a moderate temperature flame. Too hot a flame damages the phosphor coating and results in discoloring or dimming over time. Extremely hot flames thin or burn the coating from the tube showing the glowing inert gas color. This is called "highlighting" and is undesirable in signage. Taking a little longer and bending in a cooler flame remedies most highlighting.

Phosphor coating within a seam causes leaks. So before welding, remove a few millimeters of coating from the rim of each tube. Angle the tube downward then press a large cork edge gently against the rim. Rotate the tube. The cork edge removes a thin line of powder helping to keep the coating from the seal.

Classic or exotic tubes are made of soda glass. Soda glass is very expensive and cools rapidly leading to strain and breakage. Preheating a length of tubing surrounding the seam helps reduce risk of strain. Do this by passing an inch or two of each tube through the flame several times. Form the seam then quickly straighten the tube while still molten. Allow the weld to cool completely before moving unless a bend is to be placed near the weld. Then, try forming the bend while the weld is still very hot to lessen chance of strain.

Reduction Welds

A reduction weld is simply the joining of different diameter tubes. Reduction welds commonly are used on electrodes. Neon shops buy electrodes in boxes of one hundred. Were a shop to keep all sizes of both tubulated and non-tubulated electrodes in inventory, a substantial investment would be required. As such, most shops keep two or three sizes in stock and expect the glassblower to match tube sizes as needed.

A reduction weld is made by rotating the large diameter tube in a flame letting gravity shrink the molten tube end. When the diameters match, the small tube is heated and normal welding procedure followed. Instead of setting the joined tubes on the table they are held and rotated until nearly rigid to keep the tubing straight. Flaring the small tube instead also works.

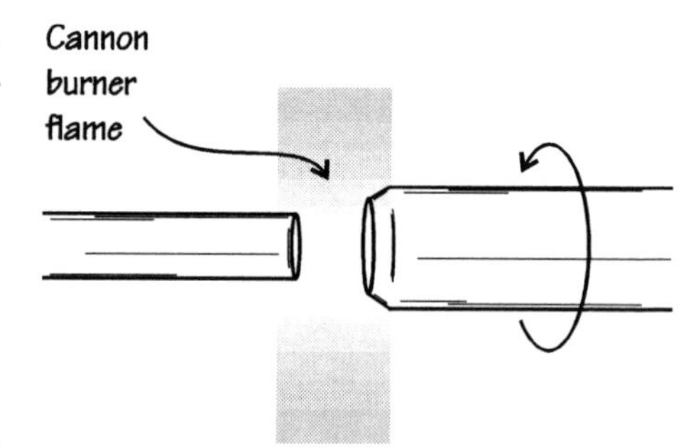

Figure 4-5
Reducing tube diameter - reduction welding

Tubulation

Tubulation is a small tube, usually five millimeters in diameter, welded into the side of a large tube. The tubulation is used as a passage through which impurities are removed from a neon unit and rare gases introduced.

Not all neon tubes get tubulated. Some use an electrode that has a tubulation built in; it is called a tubulated electrode. Tubulated electrodes pull all impurities from one end of a unit. This is considered by some inefficient. For this reason, tubulated electrodes are commonly used on short units made of fifteen linear feet of tubing or less.

Figure 4-6 Tubulation types

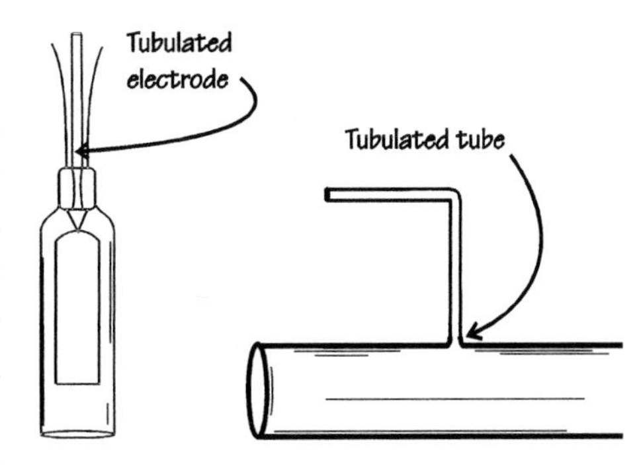

Long neon units are tubulated somewhere near linear center. This allows the vacuum pump the best chance to remove impurities by pulling equally from the unit middle. The pumping system quality and capacity determine whether a unit need be tubulated. A neon unit surpassing pumping system capability continually flickers during bombarding or does not light at all.

The Tubulating Process

Successful tubulating takes practice. It is detailed work requiring a steady hand, concentration and keen eye. Pay particular attention to handtorch position throughout the following explanation.

Seal the end of twelve inches of five millimeter tubing by inserting a pipe cleaner. Heat a couple inches from the tube open end and let gravity form a right angle. Affix a blowhose to one end of a large diameter tube and cork the other end. Mark where the tube is to be tubulated. Preheat on both sides of the mark a two inch section by passing a handtorch back and forth across this length. Rotate the torch one-quarter turn every two or three passes. Keep the torch handle nearly parallel to the large tube during this process, heating for ten or fifteen seconds.

Next, focus the tip of one flame in the middle of the preheat until it glows. The glass wall is thick initially so let the glass glow for four to six seconds. Then pull the torch away and blow hard into the blowhose. A bulge or mound will develop at the point of heat. Immediately return the flame to the mound. The glass is thinner now and only three to four seconds of heating is needed. Again remove the torch, blow into the tube and increase the mound height. When the mound is about one-quarter inch tall, heat the peak for a couple seconds. The glass here is very thin and excess heat only thickens it. Remove the flame and blow into the tube a five millimeter hole.

If too small a hole develops, quickly use a file to file down the mound. This enlarges the hole. If too large a hole is blown, stir the five millimeter tube around the molten mound or flare the small tube to fit after annealing the large tube.

Now position the handtorch underneath the main tube perpendicular to it. Lower the five millimeter tube one-quarter inch above the hole. Position the flame tips between the mound edges and the open five millimeter tube end. Heat both until molten by rotating the torch flame back and forth between them then gently touching the tubes together to form the seal.

Once joined, position the flame about one eighth inch below the seam and continue heating. The rising heat keeps the seam fluid without overheating the small tube. Blend the weld using standard welding methods until the seam is sealed and smooth.

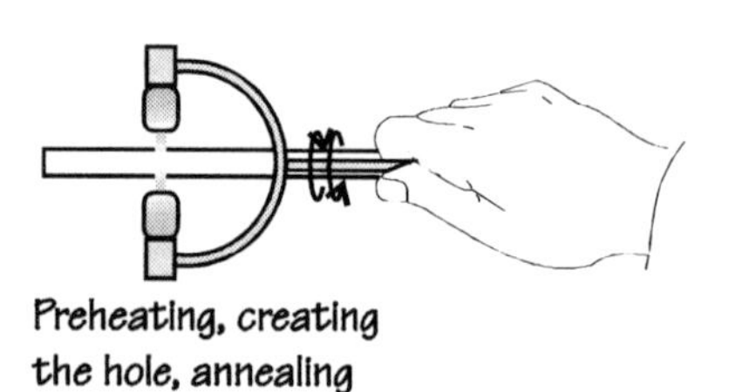

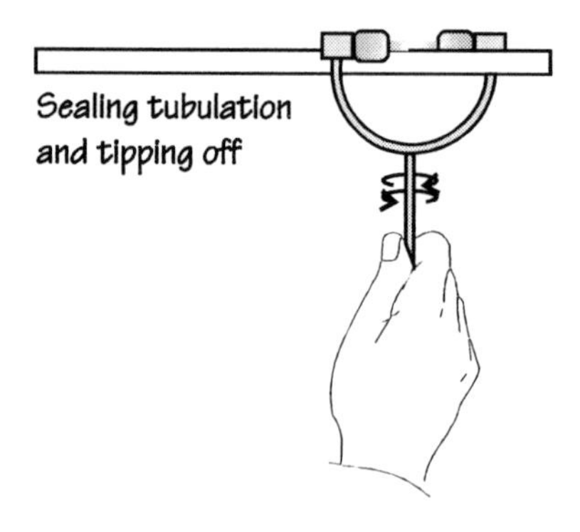

Figure 4-7 Handtorch position during tubulating

Handtorch Annealing

Annealing is cooling the glass slowly from the molten state to plastic state. The annealing procedure helps remove or spread harmlessly any strain that may have developed while working the glass.

To anneal, bring the torch into preheating position and while the seam is still molten, make slow passes back and forth across the large tube. Rotate the torch one-quarter turn every two passes heating about one inch on each side of the tubulation. After four or five complete passes, increase the stroke length to two inches on each side of the seam. Then make a final few passes about three inches on either side. Keep the motion methodical with increasingly longer strokes; never use random motion or decreasing strokes. The point is to slow the cooling rate to eliminate strain.

Common Tubulating Errors

The most common tubulating errors are excessively stretching or gathering molten glass within the seam. Stretching thins the glass and weakens the seal whereas gathering causes uneven cooling and strain. Learn to recognize these problems as they develop and correct them quickly. If the seam thins, slowly push the tubes together in increments to thicken it. If the seam is thick, slowly pull the tubes apart in increments to thin it then continue working.

Tipping-Off

Tipping-off is simply sealing the tubulation. Even after it is gassed, a neon unit is under high vacuum, about one seventy-fifth normal atmospheric pressure. This pressure collapses molten tubulation tubing sealing it. Sealed incorrectly the tip-off may leak or break. As such, care is used when tipping-off.

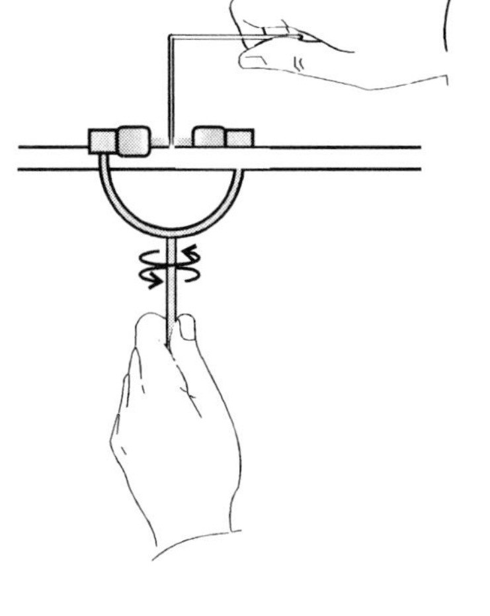

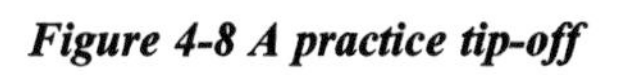

Figure 4-8 A practice tip-off

To perform a tip-off, rotate the handtorch about one-quarter inch above the tubulation weld. As the tube collapses, pass the torch back and forth across it to slow melting. Simultaneously pull the tubulation tubing until the tip-off point is about two millimeters across. Now position one flame tip at this reduced point. Quickly pull the remaining tubing away from the neon unit. Keep the torch with the unit; do not follow the residual tubing. The result is a strong, unobtrusive nipple sealing the unit.

Exercises

Objective To begin developing precise hand and finger coordination necessary to work molten glass tubing. To promote proper glass blowing skills and troubleshooting abilities.

Discussion Working molten glass requires a certain *feel* develop. Practicing welding and tubulating techniques helps cultivate this feel.

Procedure Using either a crossor cannon fire, practice the following welding techniques in twelve millimeter through fifteen millimeter clear then coated tubing. Practice both welding and tubulating using the handtorch.

When welding in a crossor cannon fire, stand comfortably with feet shoulder width apart and arms bent but relaxed at the sides. Hold the tube palms up so rolling the tube from thumb to fingertip is easy.

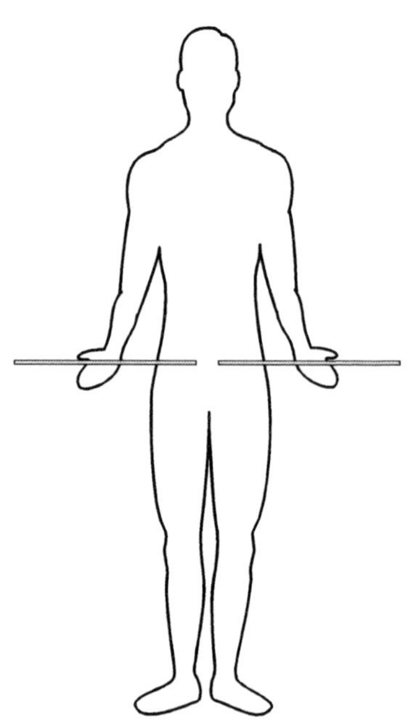

Figure 4-9 Proper stance

Welding Exercise #1

1. Cut two tubes eighteen to twenty-four inches in length. Cork the end of one tube and affix a blowhose to the end of another.
2. Hold the tubes palms up and bring the tube tips to the edge of a properly adjusted flame. Roll the tubes back and forth one-quarter turn heating evenly the ends. In or out of the flame, align and gently touch the molten tips together.
3. In the flame, roll the tube one-quarter turn until the seam glows and shrinks slightly.
4. Remove the tube from the flame and work the molten glass by sucking in then blowing out repeatedly until the glass becomes nearly rigid. Turn the tube methodically while working to insure it is straight.
5. Return to the flame and repeat steps number three and number four until the desired appearance and seal develops.
6. Heat the glass to molten one last time before setting it on the table. This assures sufficient time to straighten the tube and smooth the seam before it reaches strain temperature.
7. Quickly straighten the tube by pressing it once between two blocks and blow into the tube if needed to assure proper diameter.

8. Allow the glass to *table anneal.* Let it cool for forty to sixty seconds before moving it. WARNING! Hot glass can burn. The tube remains extremely hot to the touch for about three minutes.
9. Upon cooling, cut the tube and repeat the welding procedure. Place each weld about two inches apart. Then test a series of welds as outlined in "Testing a weld."

Characteristics of a desirable weld:

An even glass wall, no thinning or thickening of the glass.
A round and smooth seam, no rough ridges or bulges.
Even phosphor coating, no thinning due to overheating or stretching.
No leaks or cracks.

Testing a weld:

1. Visually inspect the weld for a lens effect. Look for lessening of phosphors in a coated tube. This indicates thinning the seam or pulling when working the glass tube.
2. Pass a series of welds slowly through a flame. This test checks for strain in the glass. Strained welds will shatter, so use caution.
3. Cut several welds in two. Compare the glass wall of the seam to that of the original glass wall. Check for equality.

Welding Exercise #2

1. Cut two tubes eighteen to twenty-four inches in length. Cork an end of one tube and affix a blowhose to an end of the other tube.
2. Holding the tubes palm up, bring the tube tips to the edge of a properly adjusted flame. Roll the tubes back and forth one-quarter turn to heat evenly the ends. Once softened, gently touch the tips together.
3. Continue rolling the glass in the flame one-quarter turn until the seam glows and shrinks slightly.
4. While in the flame or out; work the molten glass using jiggling or twisting methods keeping the tube straight.
5. Return to the flame and repeat steps number three and number four until the desired appearance develops.
6. Heat the glass to molten one last time before setting it on the table.
7. Quickly straighten the tube by pressing it once between two blocks and blow out if needed.
8. Allow the glass to *table anneal.* Let it cool for forty to sixty seconds

before moving it. WARNING! Hot glass can cause severe burns.
9. Upon cooling, cut the tube and repeat the welding procedure. Place each weld about two inches apart then test a series of welds.

Welding Exercise #3 Using the Handtorch

1. Cut two tubes eighteen to twenty-four inches long. Cork an end of one tube and affix a blowhose to an end of the other. Rest one tube on the table. Use a sandbag or other weight to hold it still.
2. Hold the torch as shown in Figure 4-4. Position the tube ends about one-quarter inch apart. Evenly heat the tube ends by rotating the torch one-quarter turn every second or so.
3. When the tube ends are softened, gently touch them together and continue heating the seam.
4. Work the weld by sucking in and blowing out repeatedly or by twisting or jiggling. Remove the flame as needed to maintain control.
5. When the weld is complete, heat the glass to molten one last time. Then quickly remove the weight, and move the weld onto the table for straightening.
6. Upon cooling, inspect the weld for appearance and smoothness.
7. Cut the tube about two inches from the weld and repeat the procedure. Test the welds as previously outlined.

Tubulating Exercise #1: Using the Handtorch

1. Obtain a fifteen millimeter clear glass tube thirty-two to forty-eight inches in length. Bend the tube into a U-shape using the ribbon fire, if desired. This helps makes the tube self supporting. See Figure 4-10.
2. Obtain about twelve inches of five millimeter clear tubing. Seal one end with a pipe cleaner. Heat the tube one or two inches from the open end and let gravity fold it about ninety-degrees.
3. Affix blowhose and cork to the fifteen millimeter tube.
4. Position two-thirds the fifteen millimeter tube off the table. Anchor the opposite end on the table with a sandbag or other weight.
5. Position the handtorch handle in-line or parallel to the fifteen millimeter tube. Preheat about three or four inches of the tube. Focus the tip of one flame at a single point in the middle of the preheated area.
6. After several seconds, remove the flame and blow into the blowhose. The glass will rise forming a tiny mound. Repeat this task until the mound is about one-quarter inch high. The glass thins as the mound

rises requiring less heating time on subsequent attempts.
7. Once a hole is blown, position the handtorch perpendicular to the large tube. Bring the open end of the five millimeter tubing one-quarter inch above the topless mound.
8. Position the flame between the tubes and rotate the torch one-quarter turn every second or so until the ends are molten.
9. Gently touch the molten ends together. Now, position the flame just below the seam. The rising heat keeps the five millimeter tube workable without overheating it.
10. Work the seam using either the air or jiggle technique. If the glass becomes uncontrollable, remove the flame temporarily.
11. Once the weld is complete, position the torch handle parallel to the large tube and anneal. Move the flame back and forth across the entire tubulation slowly increasing stroke lengths in controlled increments. Rotate the torch one-quarter turn every three or four passes. This cools the area slowly and evenly lessening chance of strain.
12. Now, position the handtorch handle perpendicular to the large tube. Focus the flame on the tubulation tube about one-quarter inch above the seam. Suck in on the blowhose to create vacuum and tip-off the five millimeter tube sealing it.
13. Allow the area to cool, move down the tube a couple inches and repeat the tubulating exercise. Inspect and test several completed tubulations as outlined.

Inspecting and Testing Tubulation

1. Run a file edge across the entire tubulation seam and mound to check for smoothness. Rough edges demand more heat to smooth.
2. Turn over the large tube and look through it to assure proper hole size and seam wall thickness making the tubulation.
3. With the edge of a file, tap directly on the seam. If the tubulation breaks off, inspect the remains for excessively thick or thin glass.
4. Inspect the large tube for cracks indicating improper annealing.

NOTE: When tubulating coated tubes, wiping away phosphors from the mound before sealing is not necessary. The phosphors are baked into the glass during heating. Only loose phosphors create leaks.

Also, a unit needs only one tubulation for evacuation and gassing purposes. A unit using a tubulated electrode needs no tubulating since evacuation and gassing are done through the electrode tubulation.

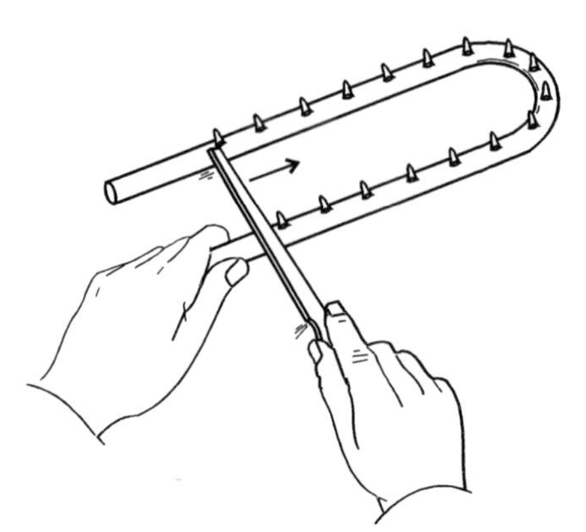

Figure 4-10 Testing practice tubulation

Tips and Tricks: Repairing Welds and Opening Tubulations

When attempting to repair a weld, slowly increase the temperature of the spliced area by moving the handtorch opposite that of annealing. That is, evenly heat a large area then slowly decrease the torch movement in controlled increments. This gradually increases the weld temperature and decreases the chance of cracking due to strain. Sometimes, it is easier to cut a weld then weld again rather than attempting to rework it.

When a weld cracks, do not remove the flame unless a piece of glass falls out. Simply repair a small crack by heating and working the area.

What looks like *smoke* on a tube is the metal lead. Too rich a flame, too much gas or not enough air, chemically reduces lead from the glass tube. Remove smoke by rotating the hot tube just above or below a flame. This area of flame contains an abundance of free electrons that act to oxidize the lead, returning it to its original state in the mixture.

When opening a coated tube for repair, assume it remains under vacuum. Unless an obvious break is visible, cutting open a vacuumed, coated tube causes air to rush in rapidly. The rushing air has sufficient force to tear phosphor coating from inside the glass wall. When a powder blown tube is renewed, the inert gas color and loose coating are visible ruining tube appearance.

To avoid this mishap, heat with a handtorch the sealed tubulation end. Ordinarily, this cracks the tip letting in a little air. After cooling, squeeze the tip-off between a thumb and index finger, gently breaking off the tip. This slows the air entering the tube and reduces chance of blowing the phosphor coating.

Other Tubulating Tips

1. Properly adjust the torch before tubulating. Test the flame on a piece of scrap tubing.
2. Keep a lighter or burning torch nearby to relight the handtorch should it extinguish during the process.
3. Think about how the unit will sit on the bombarding table before tubulating then orient and position the tubulation so it will conveniently connect to the manifold.
4. Try to tubulate somewhere near the unit center. This helps the vacuum pump remove impurities by pulling equally from the middle of the unit.
5. Let the tubulation cool for several minutes before moving to help prevent strain from developing.
6. When making a large diameter tubulation, as when building a manifold, move the handtorch in a small circle to aid forming a bigger hole. For fifteen millimeter and bigger tubulation, use a large handtorch or crossor cannon fire to heat an even larger area of glass.
7. If after blowing the hole the tubulation process is halted, anneal the area around the hole to lessen chance of strain.
8. Use pattern fabric or mica to insulate an adjoining weld or bend vulnerable to flame splash when welding. Use them as a heat barrier.

CHAPTER

5

The Basic Bends

To help form any bend, it is important to understand how angles are defined. In this text, angles between tubes or angles formed by tubes are described in degrees. See Figure 5-1 for a graphic representation. Angles range between zero and three hundred sixty degrees, from no angle to a full circle. However, most basic bends range between zero and ninety-degrees, some one-hundred-eighty degrees.

Figure 5-1 Common Angles

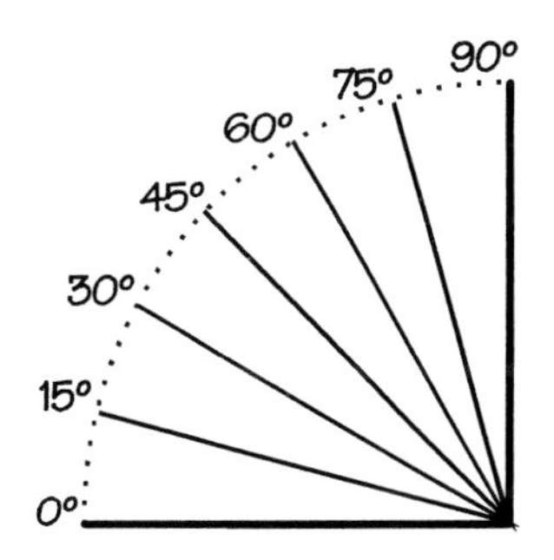

There are four basic bends used by the neon tubebender. Using these bends and slight variations, any straight-line block letter can be formed in glass tubing– the A, E, H, K, etcetera.

The L-Bend

The L-bend is found in nearly all straight-line block letters. It is a ninety-degree angle bend and is most basic of bends. To form properly an L-bend, a certain length of molten tubing is needed. If too little molten tubing is used, the glass wall stretches thin weakening the bend. Heat too much tubing and the glass sags with gravity distorting the bend. To maintain acceptable wall thickness and control, most craftsman heat an area equal to twice the tube diameter. For instance, on a ten millimeter tube heat a twenty millimeter area and on a twelve millimeter tube heat a twenty-four millimeter area. The area is marked using a glass pencil.

Figure 5-2
Marking the L-bend

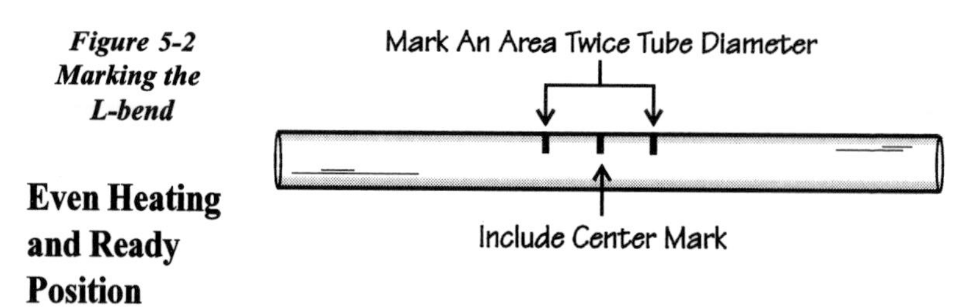

Even Heating and Ready Position

To maintain control and keep the bend from distorting, the marked area must be heated evenly. Do this by holding the tube palms up and moving the tube rhythmically in the flame. The motion is back and forth, side to side. Every couple passes partially rotate the tube one-quarter turn. To further aid even heating, bring the flame one-quarter inch or so beyond the outside marks in a crossfire. In a cannon fire, bring the outside marks into the flame middle. This assures the area between the marks is molten.

After several passes, rotate the tube one-quarter turn or ninety-degrees. Counting helps create a smooth rhythmic motion—one, two, three, four—turn, two, three, four—turn, two, three, four, and so on until the glass is molten. During the heating motion, the side to side movement never ceases. And at no point is the glass pushed or pulled though the tube diameter naturally shrinks as it softens.

Once the tube is evenly molten, face the marks upward, toward the ceiling. This is the "ready position" since the tube is ready to bend. This position aligns the molten glass with gravity easing bend formation.

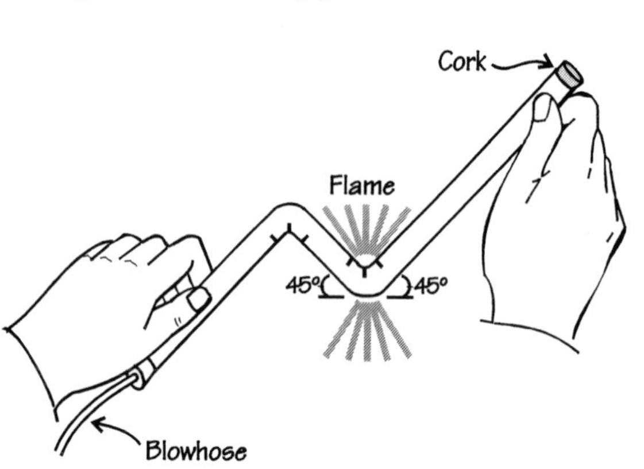

Figure 5-3
Forming the L-bend

Next, bring the tube above the fire, the flame striking the bend backside behind the center mark. Apply a second or two of heat to cool the bend inside relative to the bend backside resulting in a more uniform L-shape once blown out.

Bending, Blowing and Blocking

Remove the tube from the flame and raise both hands simultaneously toward the ceiling; form two forty-five degree angles to the floor. This evenly splits the work between hands. Ideally, the outside marks pivot in space and the hot glass hangs with gravity forming an L-shape.

Once the bend is formed, blow into the tube until the bend diameter is about one millimeter larger than original. The bend shrinks slightly as it cools so the extra size makes the bend look full upon cooling. Quickly pivot toward the table keeping an eye on the bend. Lower the bend straight down to the table and lay it over, flat. Swipe across the bend with a block to smooth and flatten it. Blow into the tube again to size if needed. Let cool forty - seconds or longer before moving or strain may develop.

Common Errors: Stretching, Pushing and Twisting

Three common errors when bending are stretching, pushing and twisting. Techniques to recognize and remedy these and other errors follow here and at the end of this chapter. Forming consistent, quality bends develops only through rote practice and learning to recognize then correct errors as they occur.

Stretching happens when the outside marks are pulled away from one another during heating or the bending motion. Stretched L-bends look rounded, not square, and the marks are further apart. If the glass wall is stretched too thin, the bend is weakened and may break. Stretching is remedied by sharpening the bend early in the motion, by pushing the outside marks toward one another then blowing.

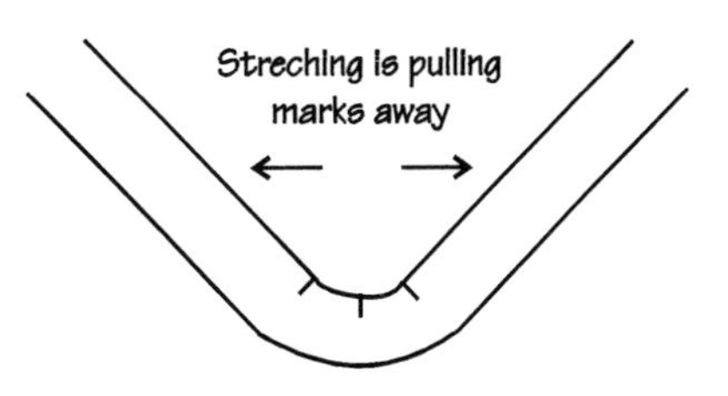

Figure 5-4 Stretching error

To correct excessive pushing, recognize the error early. A telltale "well" develops in the bend middle as the bend is formed. This well leaves excess glass or "muscles" on the inside of the bend once blown out. The excess glass cools unevenly and often develops strain. To remedy pushing, pull the outside marks away from each other before blowing into the tube. Please see Figure 5-5.

Twisting is probably the most common bending error. It is not a serious mechanical error like pulling or pushing but does affect bend appearance. If bent correctly, all pencil marks are aligned inside the L-bend, the center mark at the crease. When the marks are not aligned, twisting is indicated and a wedge shape sometimes shows across the bend. Twisting is easy to fix if caught early in the bending motion. Simply align the marks while in the ready position. Note which mark is most often rotated in a series of bends. This tells which hand is the twisting culprit.

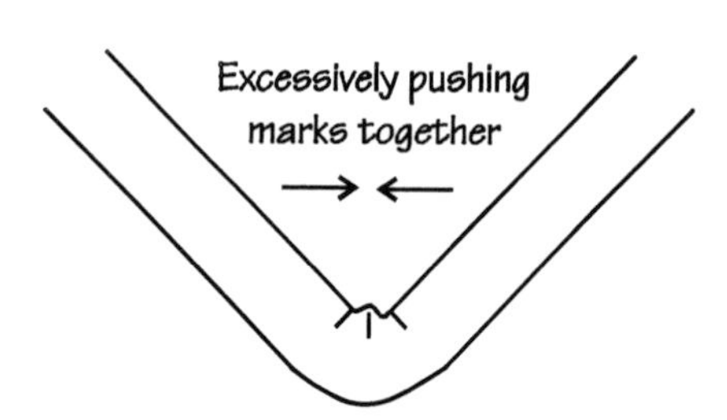

Figure 5-5 Pushing error

Avoid twisting by lifting your elbows away from your body during the bending motion. This aids keeping the wrists properly oriented and the marks aligned.

Holding Too Tight and One Hand Bending

Holding a tube lightly cures a multitude of bending sins. A good test to see if one is holding too tightly is to relax the fingers, nearly dropping the glass. If the bend swings toward you or away, the tube is held too tight and is not aligned with gravity. This causes the bend to fall out of alignment with adjacent bends.

Holding the tube lightly makes pushing, pulling and twisting movements more obvious to the touch. Fingertips sense slight motion better under less pressure, so mistakes like these are less likely to occur.

Another common mistake is one hand bending, when one hand does more work than the other does. On small tube diameters, the error is not noticeable. But large diameter tubes magnify all bending mishaps so it is important to develop good bending habits that translate from small tubes to large ones. To beat one hand bending, simply move both hands simultaneously. Divide the work evenly and gracefully between hands.

Troubleshooting a bad technique is worthwhile. Fast working glassblowers are not necessarily those who move quickly, but are those who correct mistakes as they happen.

Marking the L-bend from a Pattern

For consistency, all two-dimensional bends, bends remaining flat on the table, will be marked on the tube inside. Hence, when marking a tube for a ninety-degree bend from a pattern, make the center mark from the inside corner of the turn on the pattern. Make the mark on the tube so it ends on the bend inside corner.

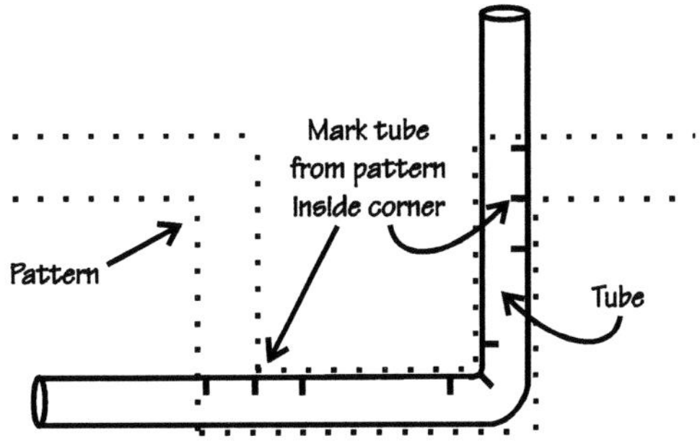

Figure 5-6 Marking the L-bend from a pattern

The U-Bend

The U-bend changes tube direction one hundred eighty degrees. It is formed both flat on the bending table and upright depending upon its function. Flat U-bends are called by this name. Upright U-bends are called “doublebacks”. Doublebacks are used to return a tube to a previous spot on a pattern or to hide electrodes behind a tube.

Heating, Bending and Blocking

To make a U-bend, heat an area about two and one-half times the tube diameter. Since the U-bend is a two-dimensional bend, it lays flat on the table. As such, mark on the side of the tube so the marks end inside the completed bend. Heat the tube to molten like the L-bend. However, instead of focusing the flame directly behind the center mark in the ready position, heat the entire backside of the bend. Apply this heat only a few passes while lifting the tubes to form the bend. This cools the bend inside relative to the backside allowing the bend to blow out more uniformly.

After forming the U-bend, both tube ends point at the ceiling. Now, blow out the bend about one millimeter larger than the tube diameter. Quickly pivot toward the table, lower the bend and lay it flat. Run a block once, flush across the top of the bend and let it cool for forty or more seconds before moving.

The space between U-bend tubes should be close to the same size as the tube diameter. That is, a tube the same diameter should lay comfortably in the trough of a U-bend. See Figure 5-7. There is an exception to this spacing rule. When making doublebacks in fifteen millimeter and larger tubing, bend spacing must be kept about twelve or thirteen millimeters. This better facilitates mounting since tube supports are only about two inches in height and a fifteen millimeter tube Doubleback is nearly two inches high, bent according to the spacing rule. Since some installations require a tube support be cut short, it is important the bend be kept tight as possible.

Space About One Tube Diameter

Figure 5-7 Proper U-bend spacing

Common Errors:
Pulling, Pushing and Twisting

The two most common errors when making the U-bend are like those when making the L-bend: pulling, pushing or twisting the glass.

Pulling a U-bend usually results in a square U-shape resembling two close L-bends. This error is easily remedied so long as stretching has not thinned the glass wall. The remedy is to move the tubes up and down alternately, much like a milking motion, simultaneously working the outside marks toward each another. This is performed while the glass is molten but may be performed even after the tube is blown out. The movement rounds the square shape.

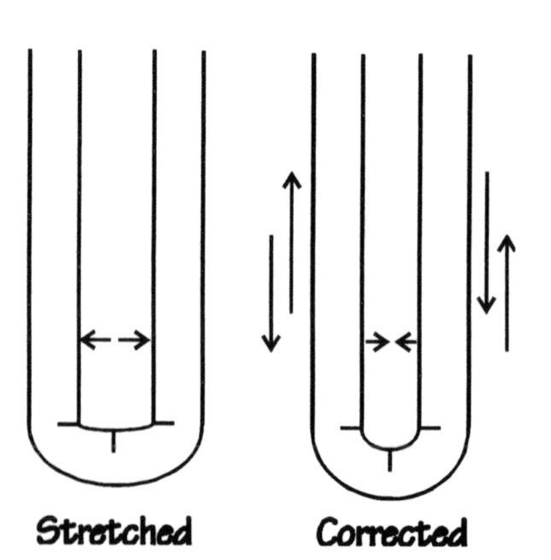

Figure 5-8 Correcting pulling error

The pushing error must be recognized and corrected before blowing out. The problem occurs when the outside marks are pushed toward each another during the bending motion. The pushing error tell-tale-sign is a well or dimple in the middle of the bend. When blown out, these create muscles or ridges inside finished bend, significantly weakening it. The best way to fix this mistake is to milk the tubing before blowing out. Do this by working the outside marks away from each other until the trough spacing is correct. The time to recognize the error and correct it must take only a couple of seconds. Figure 5-9 graphically illustrates the pushing error, how to recognize it then correct it before compromising the bend.

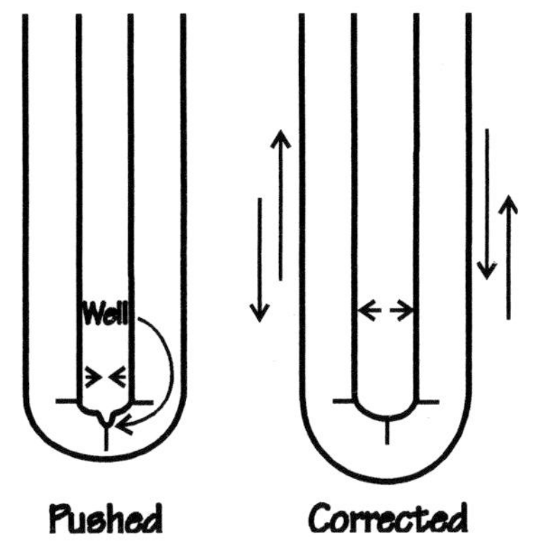

Figure 5-9 Correcting pushing error

Twisting a U-bend shows as misalignment of the marks on the bend inside. Often, an extraneous wedge shape shows across the bend. To fix twisting, hold the tube lightly and keep fingertips pointed toward the ceiling while heating. Then during the bending motion, move so the fingertips point straight at each other and move the elbows out away from the ribs. This helps keep the tubes aligned lessening chance of twisting.

Marking the U-bend from a Pattern

Marking the U-bend from a pattern is different from marking the L-bend. The center mark is made from the outside edge of the design rather than inside. The same is true when marking for a Doubleback. Compensate when marking a tube if you over-bend or under-bend the pattern.

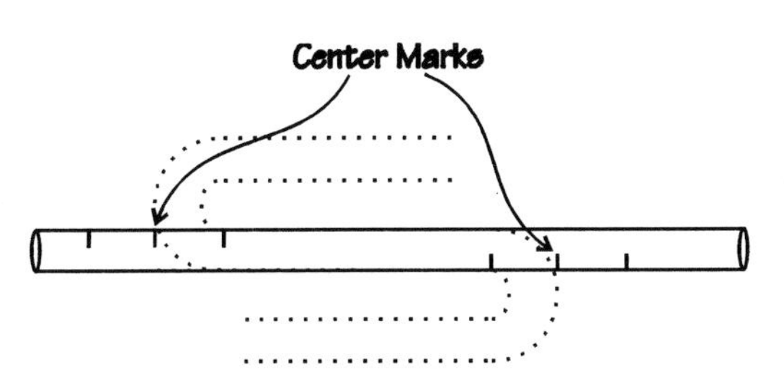

Figure 5-10 Marking the U-bend on a pattern

The Offset

The Offset is a Doubleback with an angle between the tubes. Ordinarily, the Offset is used to represent a very sharp angle, one too sharp physically to bend in glass tubing. However, it is also used when a change of elevation and direction less than ninety-degrees is needed.

Offsets are used to make letters like V, M and W.

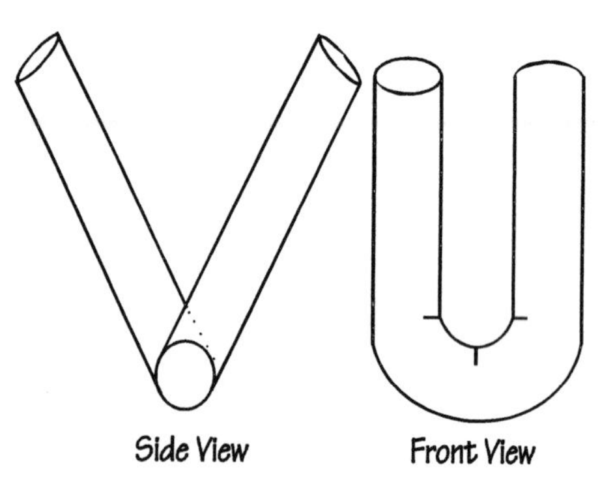

Figure 5-11 The Offset

Mark a single Offset like a U-bend, two and one-half times the diameter. Because the Offset is a three-dimensional bend, it does not lay flat on the table but changes elevation. As a basic rule, three-dimensional bends get marked on top or bottom of the tube. Bends changing elevation from table to block are marked on the tube top. And bends changing elevation from block to table are marked on the tube bottom.

To form a single Offset, heat the tube and form a U-bend. Then angle the tube in the left hand toward you and angle the tube in the right hand away. Finally, blow the bend out to proper diameter. Keep an eye on the U-shape, pivot toward the table, lower the bend and lay it over sideways. Land the tube in the right hand upon a block and the tube in the left hand flat upon the table.

To make a second Offset, mark on top the tube lying on the table a few inches down from the first bend. Pick up the marked tube with the left hand, palm up, and reach underneath to the opposite tube with the right hand also palm up. This is the ready position for the second Offset. It feels awkward but this position is maintained only a couple seconds to line up the molten tubing with gravity.

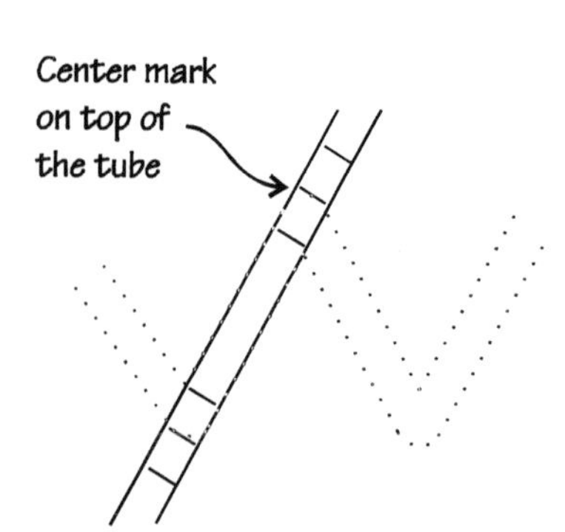

Figure 5-12 Marking the Offset from a pattern

Swing the right hand tube down and toward you to position it for heating. Let the left hand tube pivot about its axis. Begin heating the tube in the left hand by swinging the tube in the right to and fro just under the flame. When the glass is molten, point the marks to the ceiling in the ready position aligned with gravity, orient the tube in space like when it sat on the table and block.

Heat the backside of the bend a few passes then move so the tubes in each hand end perpendicular to the floor, pointing from floor to ceiling. The tube in the left hand lines up directly in front of the tube in the right hand. The Offset U-shape faces you directly. Pivot toward the table, keeping your eye on the bend, flip it over setting the tubes in each hand flat on the table. Finally, make certain the tubes are parallel before the glass stiffens.

Series Bending the Offset

For the next Offset, mark one of the tubes lying on the table on its top side. Place the marked tube in the left hand and bend again. This time move so both tube ends point upward. This assures the Offset is being formed with gravity and the tubes on each side of the bend are parallel minimizing adjustments at the table.

Because the bend is always formed in front of the tubebender, a tunnel of U-bends is formed. Indeed, placed one upon the other, a tight circular spiral can be formed. Practice the Offset with an angle between thirty and forty-five degrees between the tubes. A lesser angle makes heating adjacent bends more difficult and a greater angle demands exaggerated motion. On a properly formed Offset, the center mark is in the middle of the bend, the outside marks across from each other and a smooth U-shape connects them. There is little or no lean to the bend. In clear glass tubing, a circle nearly equivalent to the tube diameter is visible when viewed from the side.

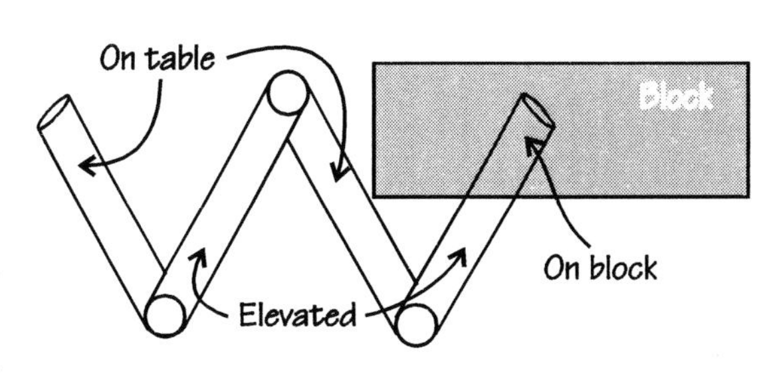

Figure 5-13 Series bending the Offset

Drops and Raises

A Raise is a change of elevation and direction ninety-degrees, from table to block height. The Raise counter part is the Drop. It is also a change of elevation and direction ninety-degrees, however, the Drop falls from block height onto the table. Because drops and raises are frequently "jumps" or connections between letters, they are not meant to be visible. As such, drops and raises are ordinarily painted out with opaque paint. In practice, the Raise is bent like a Drop and the Drop like a Raise by turning the tube over before bending. The mechanics of the bend are equal.

Bending the Right Hand Raise Toward

It is best to practice one bend in one direction until it is nearly mastered. Here we'll discuss the right hand Raise at length but only describe variations of the bend. They follow inherently from the right hand Raise discussion.

Mark the length of tubing required to form a change of elevation from table height to block height by placing the block edge against the tube. Ordinarily, this measurement ranges between two and two and one-half tube diameters depending on block height.

Heat the tube evenly to molten. Do not apply additional heat behind the center mark as with previous bends. In the ready position, lift the glass from the flame and pull a ninety-degree angle toward you, a sideways L-bend.

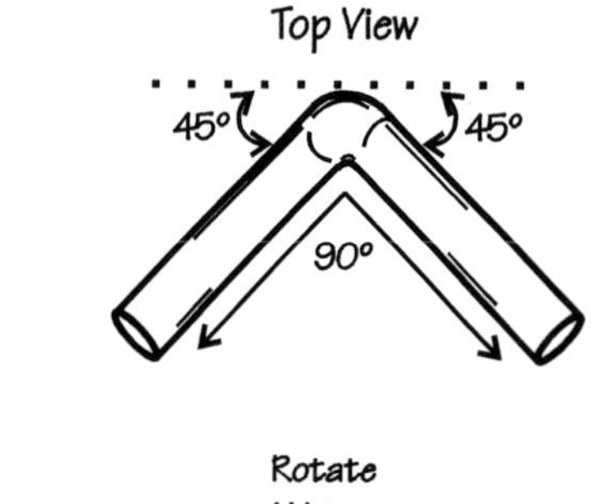

Figure 5-14 Bending a basic right hand Raise toward

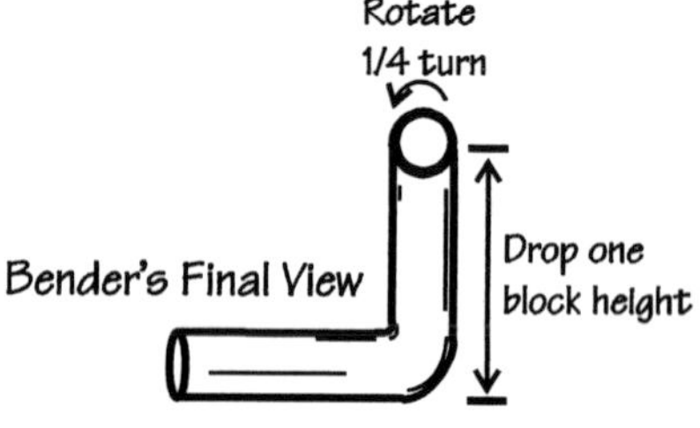

Next, drop the tube in the left hand one block height keeping all tubes parallel to the floor. Roll the right hand counter-clockwise, from your perspective, about one-quarter turn then blow the bend out. Set the tube in the right hand on a block and the tube in the left flat on the table. Let the bend cool. When mastered, this technique works well with small and large diameter tubes alike. Each hand divides the workload evenly with gravity forming a smooth bend.

Right Hand Raise Away

Once the right hand Raise is nearly mastered, it is helpful to practice making the bend away. To form a right hand Raise away, bend a sideways, ninety-degree angle away from yourself. Drop the left hand one block height and roll the right hand counterclockwise about one-quarter turn, then blow. Set the bend on the table, right hand tube on a block. Keep all tubes parallel to the floor throughout the bending motion. This assures no distortions develop when sitting the bend on the table.

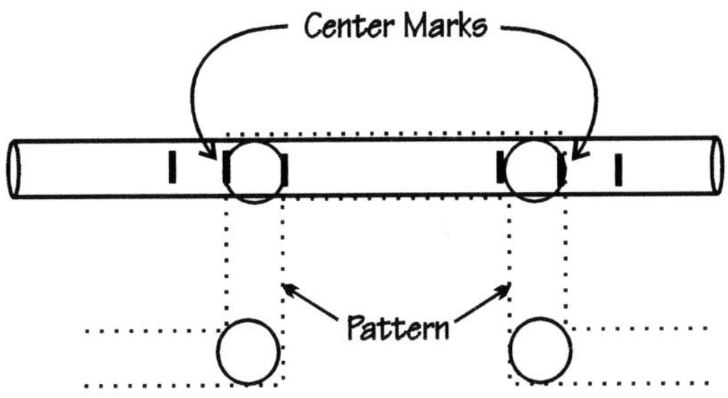

Figure 5-15 Marking raises on a pattern

To continue practicing the right hand Raise, either toward or away on the same tube, mark the tube lying on the table. Mark this tube on top to assure correct ready position. Because it is a right hand bend, always place the marked tube in the right hand.

Throughout this exercise, odd numbered bends are always placed on a block to set the change of elevation. Even numbered bends are flipped over and set flat, directly upon the table.

When working from a pattern, make the center mark at the outside point on the pattern. If the bends regularly overshoot or undershoot the pattern, compensate as needed.

Left Hand Raise

The left hand Raise is formed by placing the marks in the left hand, bending either toward or away ninety-degrees, dropping the right hand one block height, and rolling the left hand one-quarter turn clockwise.

Right Hand Drop

The right hand Drop is no more than upside-down, right hand Raise. Form it by placing the marked tube in the right hand and bend toward or away ninety-degrees. Then drop the right hand one block height and rotate one-quarter turn clockwise.

Left Hand Drop

The left hand Drop is bent with marks in the left hand, toward or away ninety-degrees, dropping the left hand one block height, and rotating the tube one-quarter turn counterclockwise.

For review the direction of rotation is:

Right hand Raise, toward or away.....counterclockwise.
Right hand Drop, toward or away.....clockwise.
Left hand Raise, toward or away.......clockwise.
Left hand Drop, toward or away.......counterclockwise.

The Leaning Raise

A leaning Raise is a change of elevation and direction that permits a tube to be brought along side the bend. It is useful when forming serif letters or when using continual bending techniques. Also, the leaning Raise allows more direction-of-bending options since some patterns are easier to bend backwards, right to left, rather than left to right.

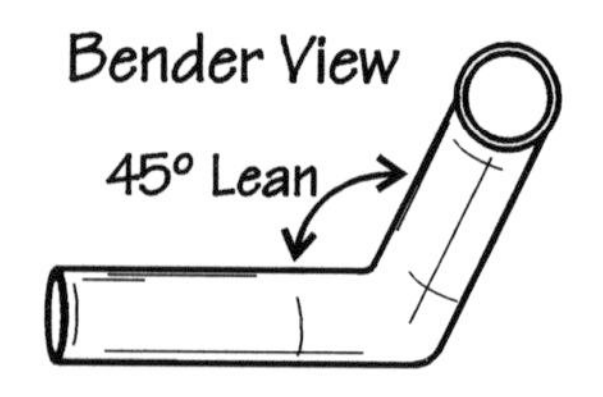

Figure 5-16 The leaning Raise

To make a right hand leaning Raise, mark the glass one tube diameter left of center but one and one-half tube diameters right of it. This allows additional glass to form the lean. Heat the tube evenly to molten, form a ninety-degree angle either toward or away, and drop the left hand one block height, then blow. Little or no rolling of the tube is required. Allow the tube to remain leaning about a forty-five degree angle one block height.

A left hand leaning Raise is bent toward or away ninety-degrees, the right hand dropping one block height and is blown out with little or no rolling. Again, the bend is left leaning about forty-five degrees.

The Straight Raise or Drop

The straight Raise or Drop is simply a change of tube elevation, not direction. It is formed by heating the glass and dropping either the right or left hand one block height then is blown out. A straight Raise followed by a straight Drop is used to create a "jump" in some letters, like to form the crossbar on the letter T. The vertical tube jumps over the crossbar tube.

Parallax

When marking any bend from a pattern, be aware of parallax. Parallax is the apparent change in position of an object when viewed from different angles. Thus, when marking a bend, look straight down beyond the tube to the pattern below before marking. Otherwise, parallax may cause you to mark the tube incorrectly throwing the bend slightly off the pattern.

Mercury Traps

Alone, argon gas lights very dim lavender, too dim for commercial use. To brighten the gas to useful levels, extremely pure, triple-distilled mercury is rolled into the tube. It is beneficial to keep the mercury away from the tube until it is completely processed. The mercury trap, a glass orb, holds the mercury droplet away from the unit until after tube processing and burn-in. Then the mercury is rolled throughout the tube.

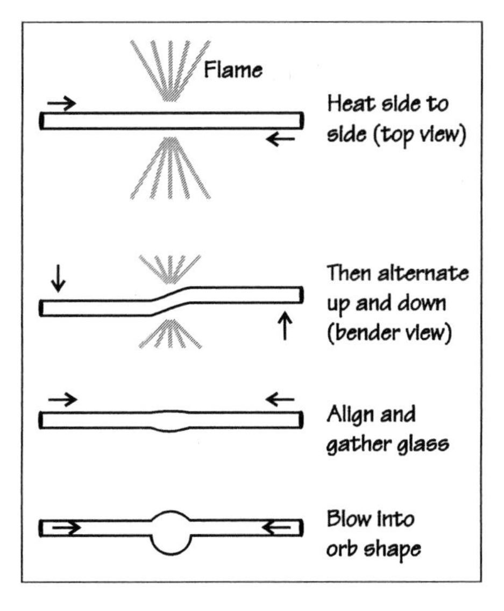

Figure 5-17 Making a mercury trap

To make a mercury trap, heat and gather about one inch of five millimeter tubing. As the tube softens, move each hand up and down in opposite directions while pushing in increments. When the glass thickens and sags, remove it from the flame and blow out carefully. A lopsided glass bubble develops. The bubble acts as a gravity well to trap the mercury. The trap is welded onto a tubulated electrode end or is tubulated into the side of a tube. A droplet of mercury is injected into the trap before tube processing.

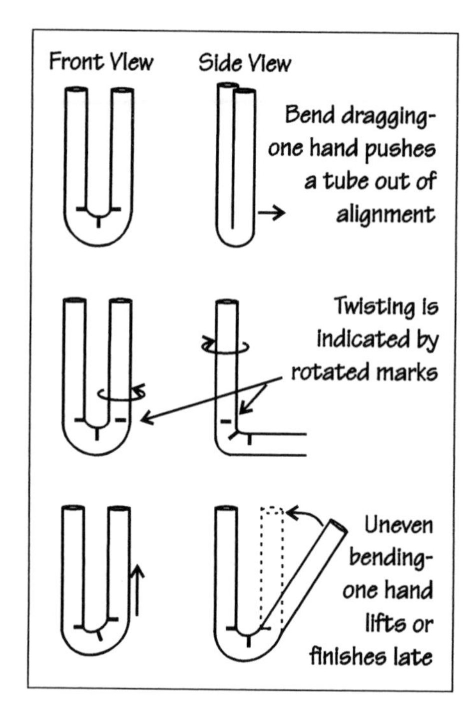

Figure 5-18 General trouble-shooting guide

Exercises

Objective To become accustom to making the four basic bends and their variations. And to become proficient at producing several consistent and marketable basic bends.

Discussion Each basic bend requires a certain length of tubing be evenly heated so the bend is formed without undue glass wall stretching or thickening. All maneuvers require both hands move simultaneously to split evenly the workload in alignment with gravity.

Procedure In either a crossor cannon fire, practice the L-bend, U-bend, Offset then Right Hand Raise in *freehand* form. Progress from twelve millimeter through fifteen millimeter clear tubing until consistent desirable results develop. Then practice bending to a pattern.

Bending Exercise #1: The L-bend

1. Begin with twenty-four inch sticks of clear twelve millimeter tubing and bend several freehand L-bends. Repeat until about seventy percent of the bends are formed smoothly with few kinks, twists or other undesirable characteristics. This may require as few as fifty bends or as many as two hundred or more.
2. Continue bending using a thirty-two inch tube then bend a full stick, a forty-eight inch tube. Remember that the goal is to become proficient at forming the ninety-degree bend, not perfect.
3. Repeat steps one and two in thirteen and fifteen millimeter clear tubing. Also try bending coated and double coated tubing.

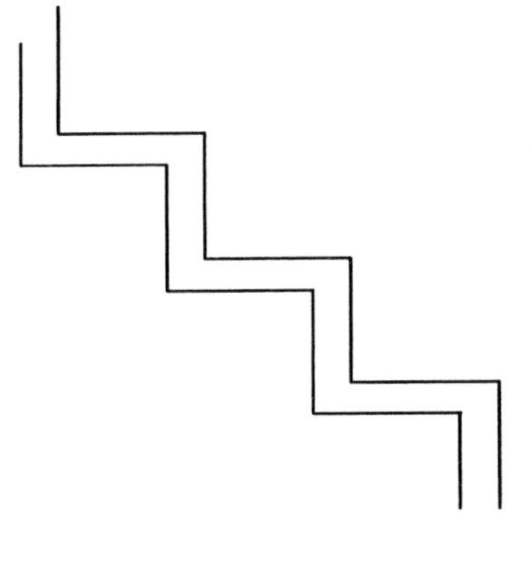

Figure 5-19 L-bend practice pattern

4. Make an L-bend pattern on heat resistant pattern material or place metal screen over a paper copy. Practice matching the tube to the design. A variation from the pattern of one-half tube diameter, about twenty percent of the time, is acceptable for a beginner. It is normal for the L-bend appearance to suffer when first bending to a pattern.
5. Move on when about seventy percent of the bends appear marketable and only twenty percent variation from the pattern.

Bending Exercise #2: The U-bend

1. Begin with twenty-four inch lengths of clear twelve millimeter tubing. Bend several freehand U-bends. Repeat until about seventy percent of the bends are formed smoothly.
2. Increase the tube length to thirty-two inches and continue bending eventually increasing the length to a full stick, forty-eight inches, and repeating the procedure. Troubleshoot improperly formed U-bends.
3. Repeat steps one and two in thirteen and fifteen millimeter clear tubing. Also, practice bending in coated and double coated tubing.
4. Make a U-bend pattern and practice matching twelve millimeter tubing to the pattern. Try to make seventy percent of the bends marketable. It is normal to see bend appearance suffer when first bending to a pattern.

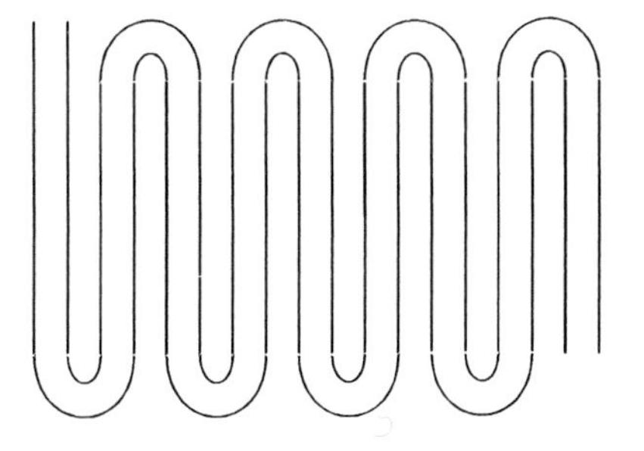

Figure 5-20 U-bend pattern

5. Move on when twenty percent or fewer bends vary one-half tube diameter from the pattern.

Bending Exercise #3 : The Offset

1. Start with twenty-four inch sticks of clear twelve millimeter tubing. Bend several Offsets freehand, no pattern. Repeat until nearly seventy

percent of the Offsets are formed smoothly with no undesirable characteristics.

2. Continue bending with thirty-two inch tubes until several consistent and consecutive Offsets result, about seventy percent marketable. Then use a full forty-eight inch stick and repeat the procedure. The goal is to become proficient at forming the Offset bend, not absolutely perfect.

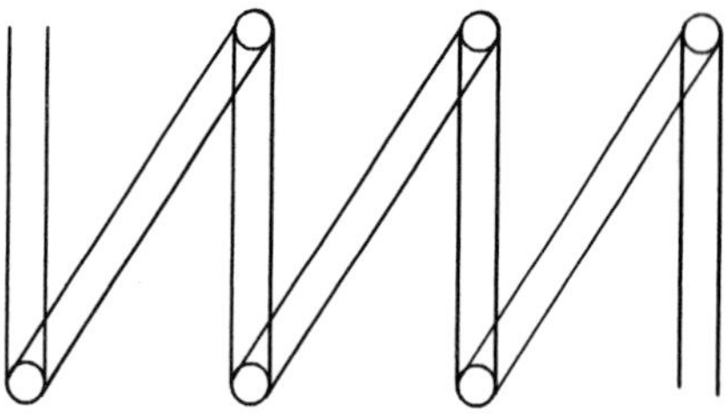

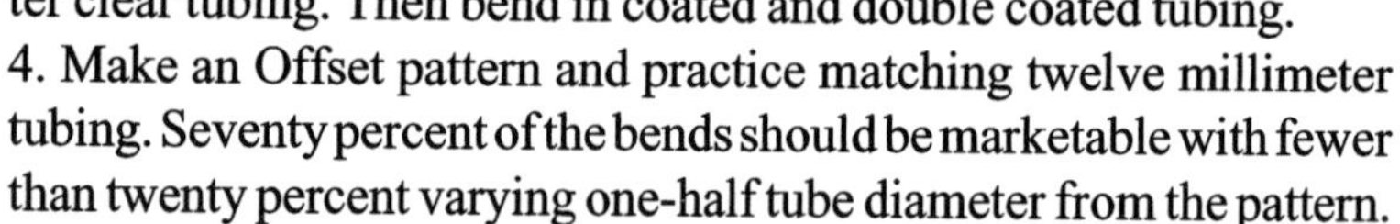

Figure 5-21
Offset practice pattern

3. Repeat steps one and two in thirteen and fifteen millimeter clear tubing. Then bend in coated and double coated tubing.

4. Make an Offset pattern and practice matching twelve millimeter tubing. Seventy percent of the bends should be marketable with fewer than twenty percent varying one-half tube diameter from the pattern.

Bending Exercise #4: Drops and Raises

1. Bend twenty-four inch, clear twelve millimeter tubing into freehand Drops and Raises. Repeat until nearly seventy percent of the bends are formed smoothly.

2. Use longer, thirty-two inch tubes, and continue bending until several consistent and consecutive Drops and Raises result. Then increase the length to a full stick of tubing and repeat the procedure. Try to become proficient at forming the drops and raises.

3. Repeat steps one and two in thirteen and fifteen millimeter clear tubing. Then bend in coated and double coated tubing if desired.

4. Make a pattern and practice matching twelve millimeter tubing. Again, about seventy percent of the bends should be marketable with no more than twenty percent varying one-half tube diameter from the pattern.

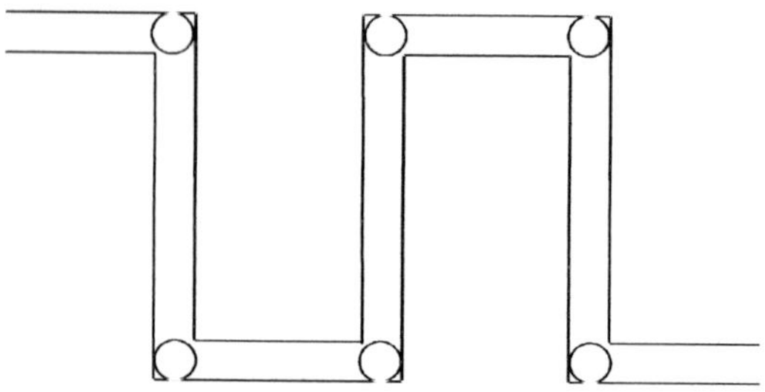

Figure 5-22
Drops and Raises practice pattern

Basic Bend Tips

1. Metal does not stick to molten glass, so some craftsman smooth the inside of a poorly formed U-bend or Offset using an electrode shell affixed to the end of a pencil. They remove the shell from a twelve or thirteen millimeter electrode and silicone it to the pencil end. Immediately after forming a poorly made bend, they roll the metal shell on the bend inside smoothing the glass, bettering its appearance.
2. Some sharpen the inside of an L-bend by pressing a file edge into the inside corner while the glass is still molten.
3. Form two close L-bends turning in the same direction in a single heat. Mark the inside corner of each bend then heat slightly beyond each mark. Form the bends using a U-bend forming motion but pulling the marks apart as you move. This removes the curve between the marks effectively forming two L-bends.
4. Form two close L-bends going in opposite directions by forming them like a flat lying, straight Raise. Heat the proper length of tube, form the straight Raise and fit the bends to the pattern.
5. Form two close Offsets in opposite directions by forming a small circle. With a blowhose, measure the length of tubing needed to form the bends and transfer this length to the tube. Heat the glass over the ribbon burner and loop it into a small circle. Flip the circle over and stand as two Offsets. This method works best using small diameter tubes, eight or ten millimeter.
6. Form a Drop and Raise simultaneously by laying molten tubing over a suitable block. Measure the length of tubing needed to form the bends and heat to dripping in a ribbon burner. Lay the glass over the block and push it to the table, then blow out to proper diameter.

Figure 5-23 Forming two L-bends at once

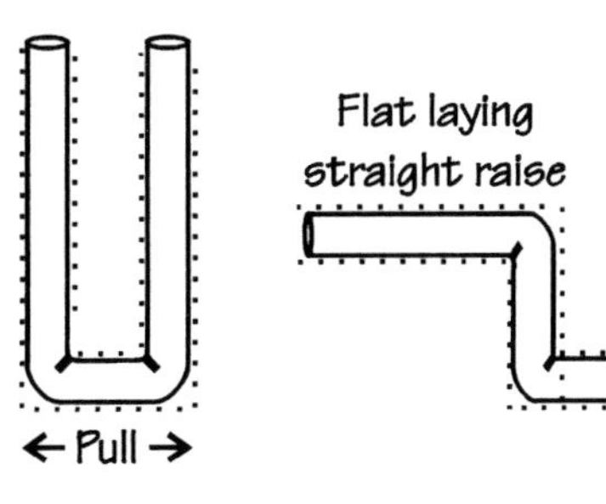

7. Use a piece of scrap glass as an extension when no tube holder is available. Simply weld the scrap on temporarily then cut off after cooling.
8. While heating a tube, hold excess blowhose loosely in one hand to keep it from entering the flame or from entangling with other objects.

Figure 5-24 and 5-25
The five basic maneuvers following tube left to right:
L-bend, U-bend, Weld, Offset and Drop/Raise
formed on metal screen over paper pattern

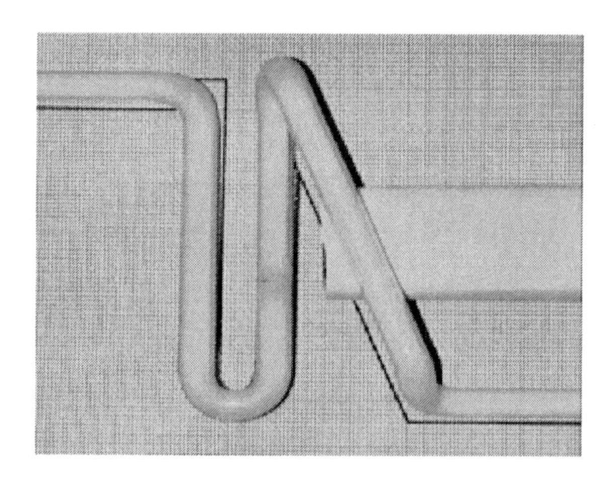

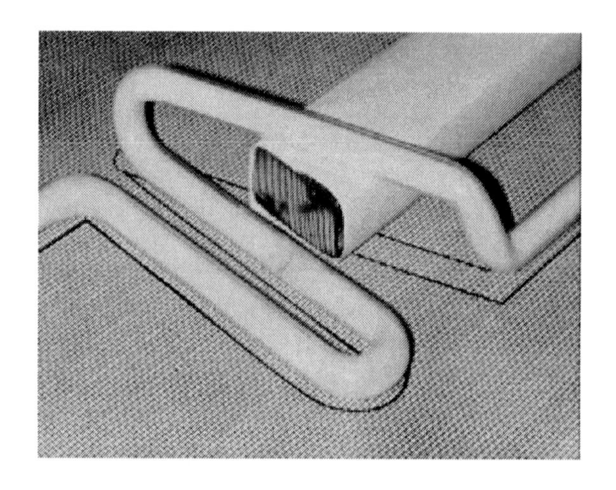

CHAPTER

6

Bending Block Letters

Knowing only the four basic bends and slight variations of these, it is possible to form straight-line block letters such as A, E, H, K, M, etcetera. Each letter may be bent several different ways. To define these different ways we will consider rules used to bend beer sign letters then develop rules to define other ways of bending.

Beer Sign Bending

"Beer Sign" style letters place all tubes destined to be visible on the bending table. Any tubes suited for blockout are bent off the table onto a block. Beer sign bending is used by beer sign manufacturers and other mass production facilities to hasten tube painting. This bending style allows them to dip finished tubes in an opaque paint quickly hiding tubes meant not to be seen. The process is not exclusive to mass production shops; many small shops use this method too.

Cadillac Letters

"Cadillac" style bending is defined as placing all lit tubes on the table and no breaks in any given line. Not all letters have a viable Cadillac version, but most do. This technique enhances the appearance of a window sign or any sign seen up close. Cadillac letters can be dipped in blockout paint too, like beer sign letters.

Commercial Style

A third style of bending letters or designs is the "Commercial" style. This kind of bending is difficult to read close-up but works well in signs displayed at a distance. Commercial style bending does not lend itself to blockout dipping and is not shown in the following examples.

Bending Accuracy

Bending accuracy is more important when making small letters or designs because any variation from the pattern is a larger percentage of the whole. Thus, a one-quarter inch deviance on a two inch letter is more noticeable than on a twelve inch one.

First Rule of Thumb

The first rule of thumb when bending is to begin bending the inside first. This helps prevent bending oneself into a corner. Put another way, this helps prevent overlapping tubes. Overlapped tubes can force a cut in the letter face to ease further bending. This results in an unnecessary, unsightly face weld and is a direct result of lack of planning. Following the first rule helps one avoid overlapping tubes.

Block Letter Layout

The following illustrations offer bend-by-number methods for forming straight-line block letters. Not all letters are shown as some are easily derived from those offered: the F from the E, the I from the H, the W from the M, etcetera. The designs are drawn backwards, or mirror image, so the face of each glass letter is flat when viewed from the front. All neon tubes are bent in this fashion.

Circles indicate a change of tube elevation, one block height, and direction as indicated by the pattern. Dashed lines indicate bends or tubing below a tube and where a heat begins and ends.

Curved Block Letters

Block letters made of curves require use of a ribbon burner. It is used to form smooth flowing curves. On very small curves, consider using a crossor cannon fire instead of the ribbon since some ribbon burners do not heat evenly on short lengths.

Measuring and Marking

The blowhose is frequently used to measure a length of tubing required to form a curve. This is done by marking the pattern where a curve begins and ends. The blowhose is positioned around the curve noting the length mark to mark and the measure transferred to the appropriate position on the tube.

For consistency, mark the tube on the inside of the curve. When in the ready position, the marks will point upward as before. The proper ready position allows gravity to aid forming a smooth curve.

Second Rule of Thumb

The first rule of thumb for bending letters or designs is to bend the inside first. The same is true of curved letters or designs with one addition. If there exists a ribbon fire curve that aids forming the inside of the letter or design, bend it first.

Letter Layout and Style Notes

The following illustrations offer variations for bending curved block letters. Not all letters are shown as others follow logically from these and prior examples.

Some letters use a curve to tuck another bend into place. These curves are labeled "curve tuck" bends. Other letters use a ribbon curve to fold two halves of a letter together. They are called "curve fold" bends. In some cases, it is feasible to break a curve into two or more heats or to form two curves in one heat. It depends upon the size of the curve and the craftsman skill level.

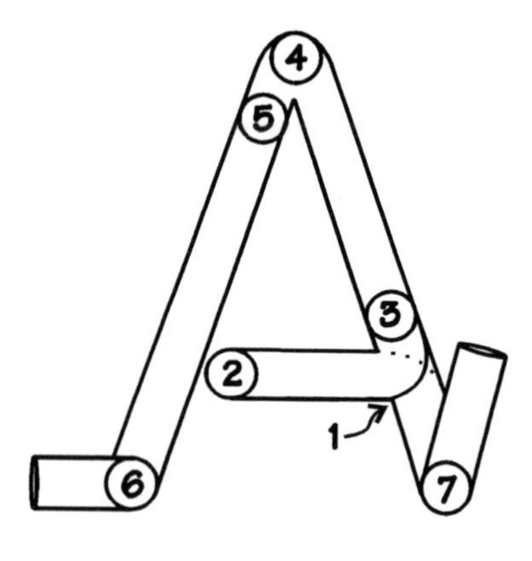

Beer Sign A

1. L-bend
2. Doubleback
3. Drop
4. Offset
5. Straight Drop
6. Raise
7. Offset

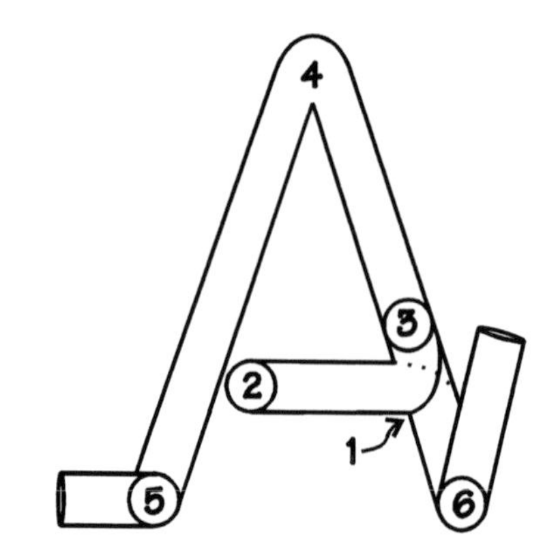

V-bend A

1. L-bend
2. Doubleback
3. Drop
4. V-bend
5. Raise
6. Offset

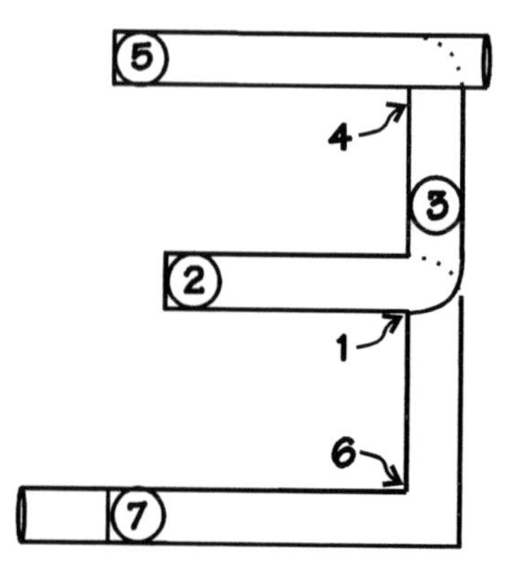

Beer Sign E

1. L-bend
2. Doubleback
3. Drop
4. L-bend
5. Doubleback
6. L-bend
7. Straight Raise

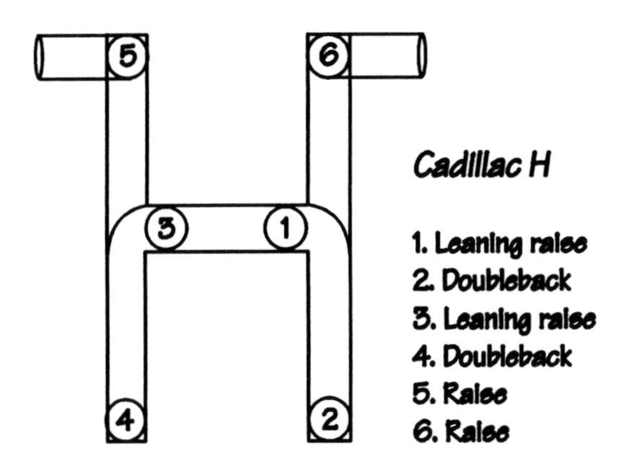
Cadillac H
1. Leaning raise
2. Doubleback
3. Leaning raise
4. Doubleback
5. Raise
6. Raise

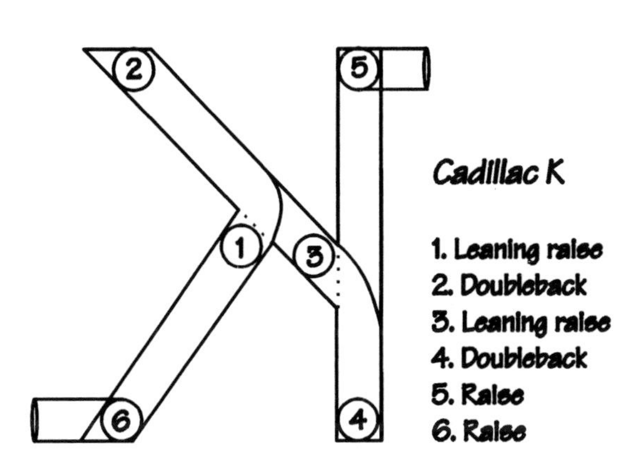
Cadillac K
1. Leaning raise
2. Doubleback
3. Leaning raise
4. Doubleback
5. Raise
6. Raise

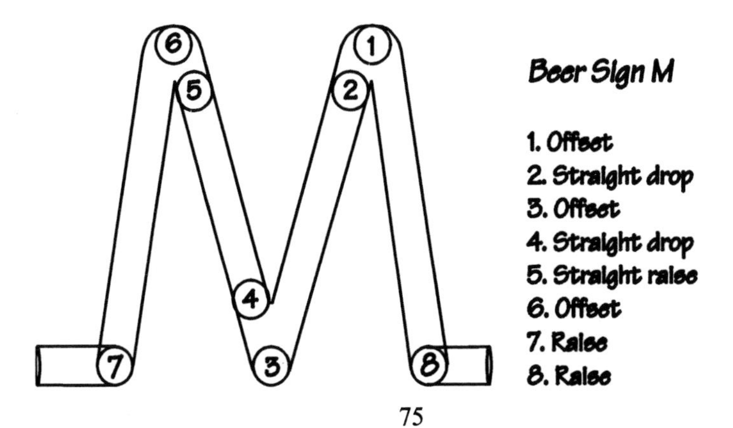
Beer Sign M
1. Offset
2. Straight drop
3. Offset
4. Straight drop
5. Straight raise
6. Offset
7. Raise
8. Raise

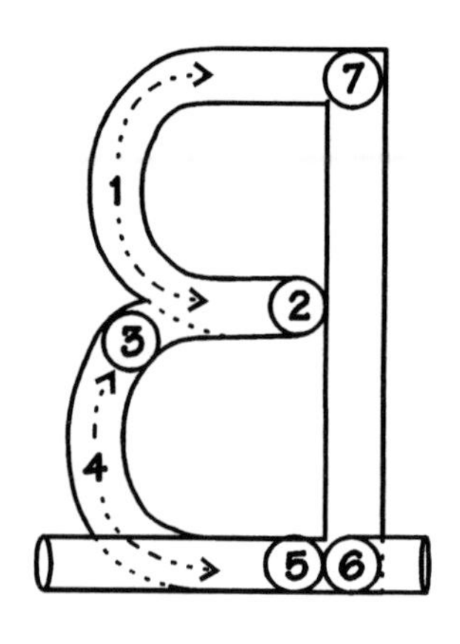

Beer Sign B

1. Curve
2. Doubleback
3. Drop
4. Curve
5. Doubleback
6. Raise
7. L-bend fold

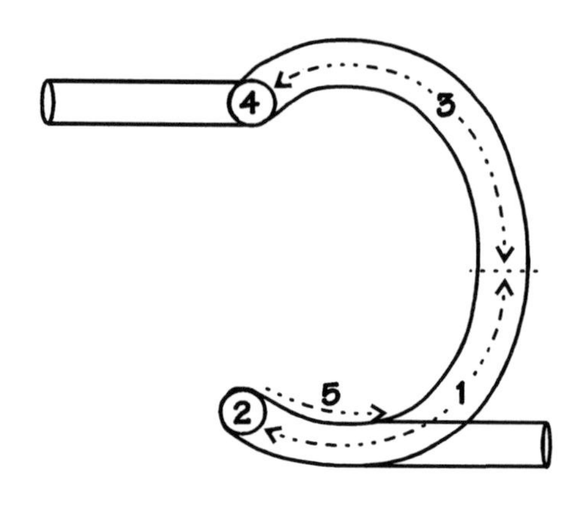

The C

1. Curve
2. Doubleback
3. Curve
4. Raise
5. Followback

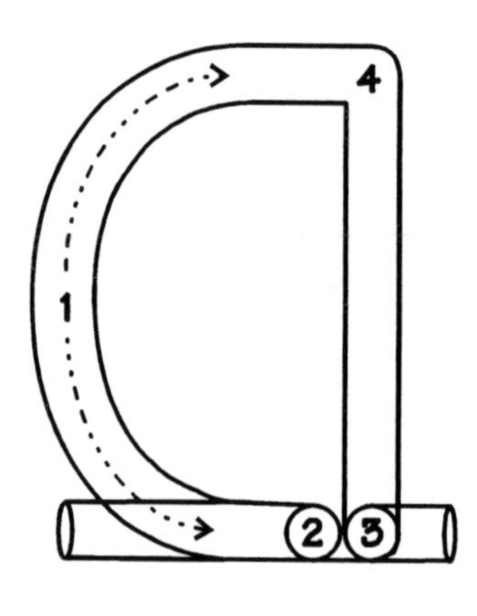

The D

1. Curve
2. Doubleback
3. Raise
4. L-bend fold

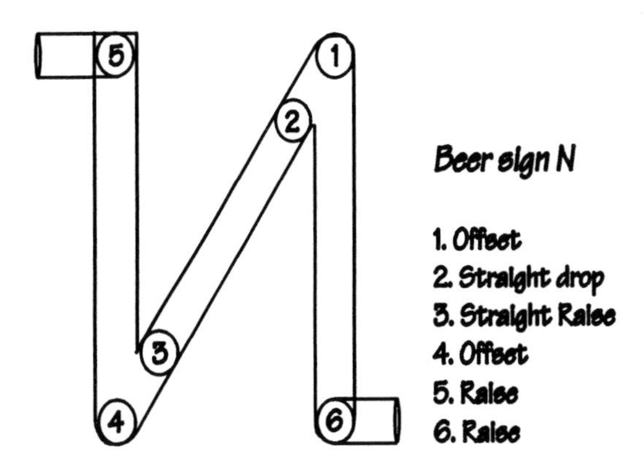

Beer sign N

1. Offset
2. Straight drop
3. Straight Raise
4. Offset
5. Raise
6. Raise

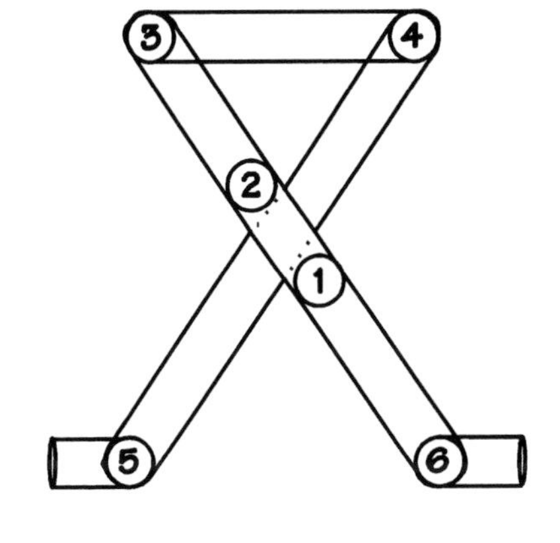

Beer Sign X

1. Straight Raise
2. Straight Drop
3. Offset
4. Offset through jump
5. Raise
6. Raise

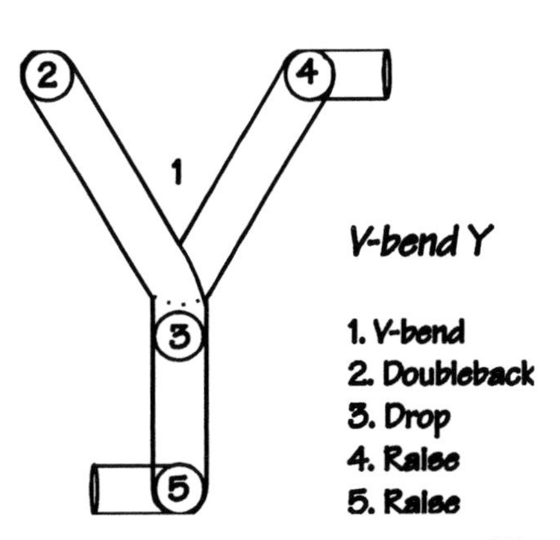

V-bend Y

1. V-bend
2. Doubleback
3. Drop
4. Raise
5. Raise

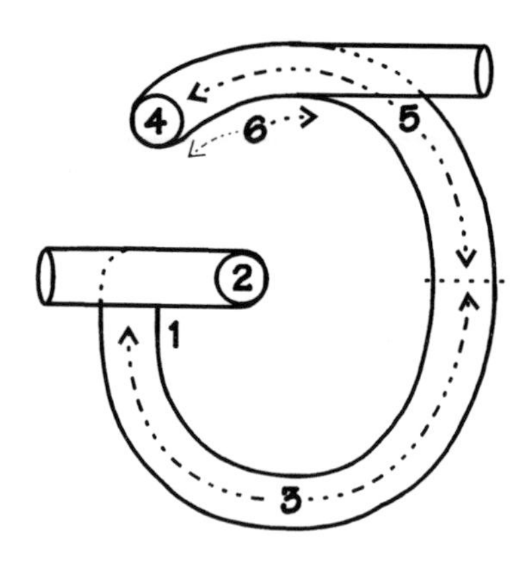

The G

1. L-bend
2. Doubleback
3. Curve
4. Doubleback
5. Curve tuck
6. Followback

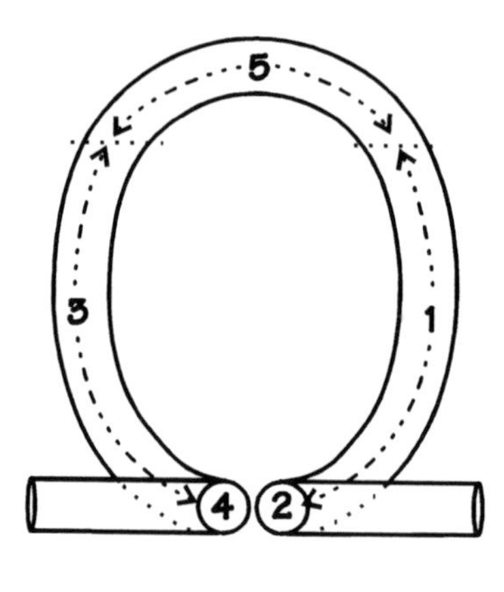

The Split O

1. Curve
2. Offset
3. Curve
4. Offset
5. Curve fold

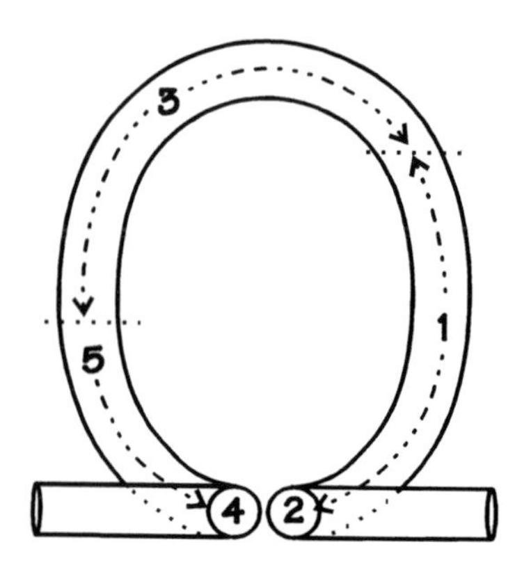

Other Split O

1. Curve
2. Offset
3. Curve
4. Offset
5. Curve tuck

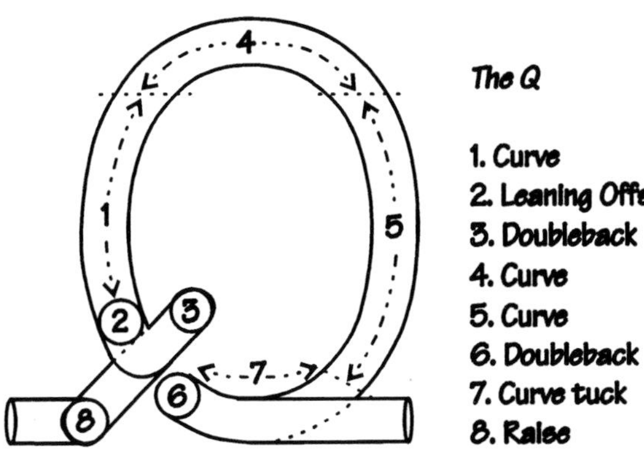

The Q
1. Curve
2. Leaning Offset
3. Doubleback
4. Curve
5. Curve
6. Doubleback
7. Curve tuck
8. Raise

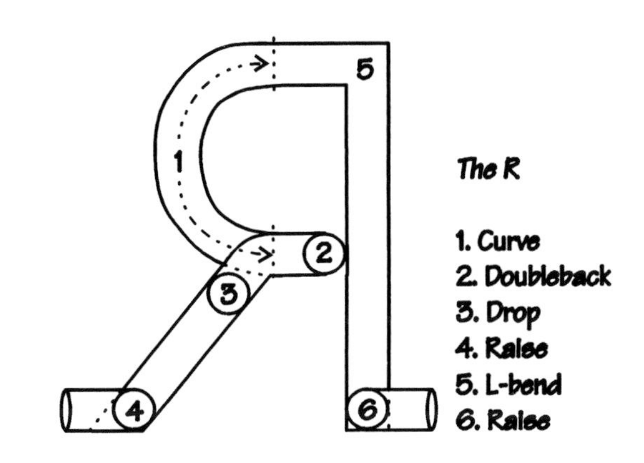

The R
1. Curve
2. Doubleback
3. Drop
4. Raise
5. L-bend
6. Raise

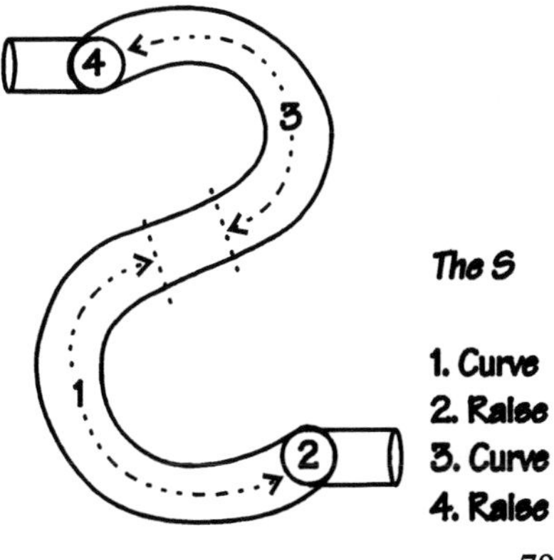

The S
1. Curve
2. Raise
3. Curve
4. Raise

Continuous Bending

When bending any sign it is desirable to reduce the number of welds. Not only does this save manufacturing time, it also limits the number of possible leaks. The bending technique for minimizing welds and effectively using tubing is called continuous or continual bending. It involves using as much tubing as possible before cutting and welding. Continuous bending requires planning and an ability to place bends ahead of sequence.

Most block letters, six inches in height or less, lend themselves well to continual bending techniques since many letters can be bent from a single length of tubing. Careful measuring with either a blowhose or mapping wheel determines how many letters can be bent before running out of tubing. The craftsman uses this information to plan where welds will be placed, trying to position them in a blockout area.

The Continuously Bent OPEN Sign

Consider a simple six inch, block letter OPEN sign. Careful measuring shows the O and P can be bent continuously, the same of the E and N. A single weld pieces them together between the P and E.

After bending the O, bend the vertical leg of the P into place. However, save the L-bend at the top of the P as a pivot point. Hold the L-bend center mark in position and swing the remaining unbent tubing across the top of the letter–saving the L-bend as a pivot point moves previous bends out of the way. This enables you to finish the remainder of the P then fold all together using a simple basic L-bend.

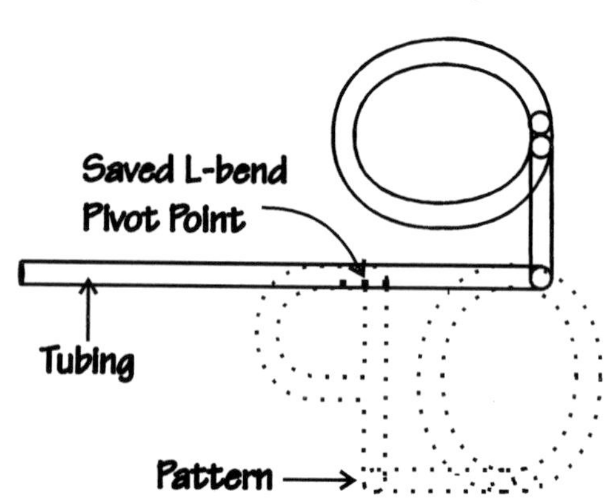

Figure 6-19 Continuous bending the O and P

To continuously bend the E and N, begin bending at a point that is either familiar or balanced. So, start with the middle L-bend of the E since it is familiar. First, measure from the end of the tube of the letter P to the middle L-bend of the E. Then add one

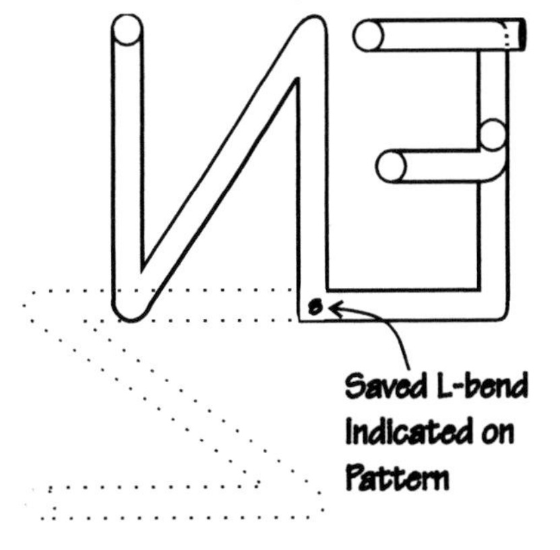

inch overlap between the P and E as precaution. This assures the letters will meet. Begin bending the E at this predetermined point on the tube.

Figure 6-20 Folding the E and N

After forming the middle and top of the E, bend the lower portion. Then when bending the N, the tube flows away from the E. Hence, the N is bent in normal sequence, no folding is required. Still, some save the L-bend to make bending the N easier for them.

It is best to save an easy basic bend to fold letters together using continual bending techniques. An advanced glassblower can L-bend, U-bend, and even Offset a unit together–often, saving two or three consecutive bends for folding.

The Curve Fold

Curves are also used in continuous bending. A ribbon curve is sometimes saved to fold two or more complex pieces together. Consider a serif letter U. Bending each serif after forming the ribbon curve causes tubes to overlap hindering further bending. However, by saving the U shape for last, overlapping is prevented.

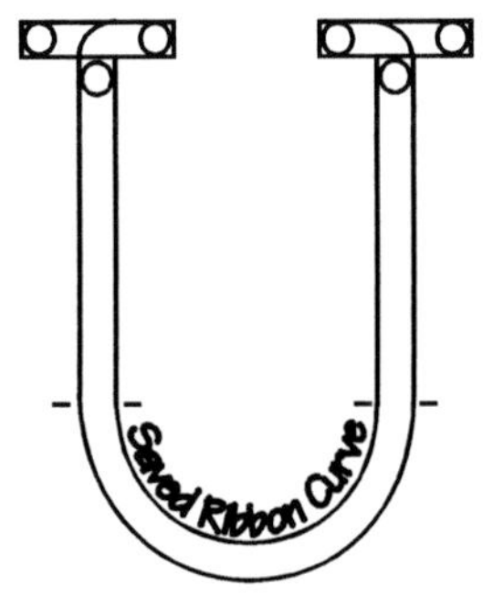

Figure 6-21 Using a ribbon curve for folding

With experience, one develops the skill of "thinking in neon." You mentally bend a sign sequentially working out the details of bending before putting the glass to the pattern.

Common Continual Bending Sequences

No two craftsmen may execute the same bending sequence in a given sign–preference and ability determine the sequence. There is no right or wrong way of bending so long as the glass is not strained nor stretched and fits the pattern.

Some continual bending sequences appear regularly, like saving an L-bend or a Doubleback for folding, see Figure 6-22. Hence, mastering only a couple continual bending maneuvers goes a long way to saving both time and materials.

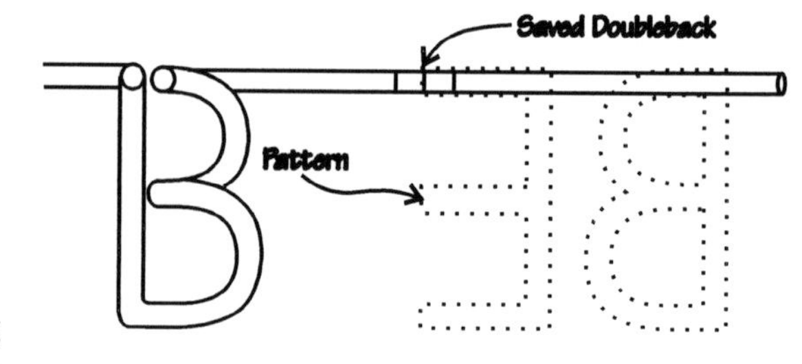

Figure 6-22 Saving a Doubleback for folding

Even welding on electrodes first then forming the bend to position them, is faster than forming the positioning bend, waiting for it to cool, then welding on the electrode. And when saving a Drop or Raise for folding, think of the bend as a ninety-degree Offset. This effectively eliminates the confusing roll during bend formation.

Always use a mark on the blowhose or a map wheel to determine where a tube will end on a pattern before bending. This helps to position welds in blockout areas. While measuring and mapping the pattern, consider which bends will cause tubes to overlap. Then find a previous basic bend and use it to fold the piece together avoiding overlapping tubes.

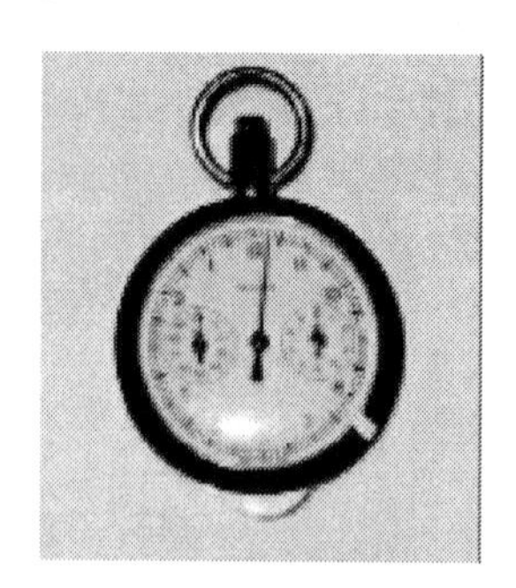

Figure 6-23 The map wheel

Figure 6-24 shows one way to bend continually a small window sign made of two units. The sequence efficiently eliminates overlapping tubes during bending. The only welds are the welds used to attach electrodes. Note the bends made out of sequence for continual bending purposes.

Figure 6-24 Continual bending a two unit sign

1. L-bend
2. Doubleback
3. Leaning Drop
4. L-bend
5. L-bend
6. Doubleback
7. Drop
8. Leaning raise
9. Doubleback
10. Leaning offset
11. Doubleback
12. Raise
13. Drop
14. L-bend
15. Leaning drop
16. Doubleback
17. V-bend
18. Offset
19. Drop
20. Leaning drop
21. Doubleback
22. Weld
23. Raise
24. Weld
25. Offset

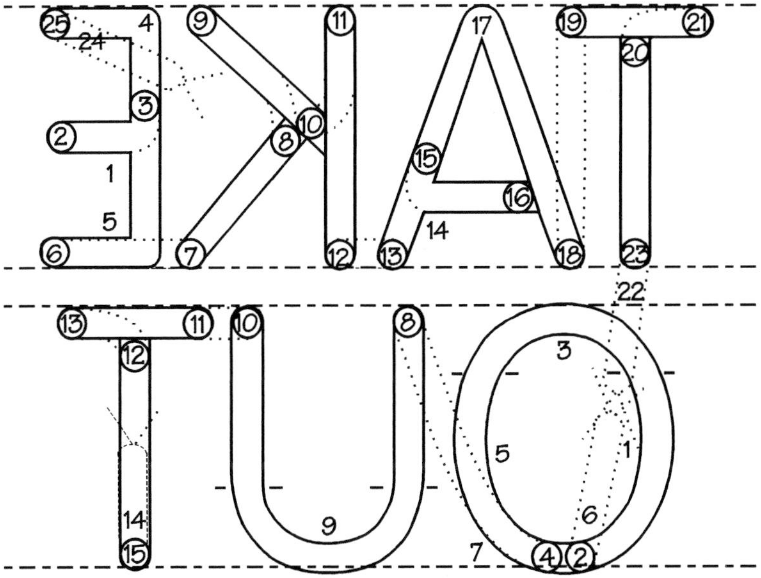

1. Curve
2. Offset
3. Curve
4. Doubleback
5. Curve
6. Weld
7. Followback
8. Offset
9. Curve
10. Raise
11. Drop
12. Leaning drop
13. Doubleback
14. Weld
15. Doubleback

Exercises

Objective To become familiar with basic bends and variations used to form block style letters.

Discussion There are many ways to bend a letter or design. No one way is necessarily right. However, certain conventions make forming quality block letters easier.

Procedure Enlarge the provided letter layouts with a projector or copier and practice bending each block letter. Then try other variations based on your understanding of the methods described.

Helpful Hints for Bending Block Letters

1. Properly adjust all flames.
2. Clear the bending table of unnecessary items. Keep tools nearby.
3. Rotate the pattern to best facilitate positioning a bend at the table.
4. Connect the blowhose to the most stationary part of tubing during a maneuver. This helps keep the blowhose from passing through a flame or entangling on equipment.
5. Place a mark on the blowhose at four linear feet or use a map wheel to determine needed tube length.
6. Blow into the blowhose before entering a fire to ensure an air seal.
7. Position tube labels, manufacturer name and tube color, in blockout areas or on the letter back. This leaves the letter face unblemished. Some markings burn off in the fire. Others can be removed with acid etching cream or other dilute acid. All tube labels are marked the tube color when filled with argon and mercury, not when neon gas filled.
8. Compare your best-bent letters with those found in the marketplace, in window signs and on pole signs.

CHAPTER

7

Basic Pattern Making

A Worthy Design

The first step to making a quality neon sign is working from the finest design possible. Large shops ordinarily have a professional sign designer on staff. For them, generating an eye catching and effective sign is part of the job, and they charge for it. Small shops might rely on a design studio, another sign company or other resource.

Design studios produce high quality but sometimes high priced work. If a project justifies the expense, then this is the most advantageous path toward a worthy design. These professionals are tuned to design trends that may translate well into neon.

A less expensive path is to work with a sign painter or vinyl shop worker. They are experienced sign designers who produce effective and modern depictions like a design studio.

Some shops keep all design in-house. The average personal computer runs easily professional graphic design software. Though the software does not replace a design expert, it offers tools to become one. Often filled with hundreds or more design samples, these programs significantly lower the learning curve toward becoming a sign designer.

Figure 7-1
Computer programs to aid pattern design
(courtesy Neon Wizard)

Computer alphabets called fonts enable one to change lettering style immediately for on-screen customer approval. Creative borders, perfect circles and easy-to-make custom letters are just part of the power of computerized design. These programs drastically reduce the labor to create a pattern leaving more time for sign sales and sign making.

Completed computer depictions are easily printed as full size, reversed patterns on plotters. They can print on paper or ready for bending, non-asbestos material. Sign shops that do not own a plotter can print to a desktop printer and enlarge the design using an opaque projector then clean up and trace the design onto bending pattern material. Opaque projectors are sold in art and sign supply stores.

Figure 7-2 Opaque projector

Making a Technically Correct Neon Pattern

Once a distinct design is created and customer approved, the second step to create a quality sign is making a worthy, technically correct neon pattern. Considered in the following text are design elements and bending aids critical to executing a technically correct neon pattern.

Baselines and Angles

A baseline is an invisible line upon which all non-curved letters rest. Use a straight edge to draw the baseline across the bottom of a design. Except for curved letters, adjust all letters to meet this line. Curved letters are drawn fractionally larger than non-curved letters because they appear smaller to the human eye. They get positioned slightly below the baseline to make the image appear balanced, more legible.

If all letters are capitals, draw another line across the design top. If not, draw a line across both the top of all capital letters and all lowercase letters. Adjust the height of each letter to meet these lines allowing curved letters to extend slightly beyond.

Next, make sure all angles are equal. Align a right angle ruler with one letter keeping the right angle point on the sign baseline. Mark on the pattern the bottom tip of the opposite angle. Do this at the sign end points and connect with a line. This line is called a pointline. Slide the right angle ruler along the point and baseline to maintain letter angle throughout the design.

Figure 7-3 Maintaining lines and angles

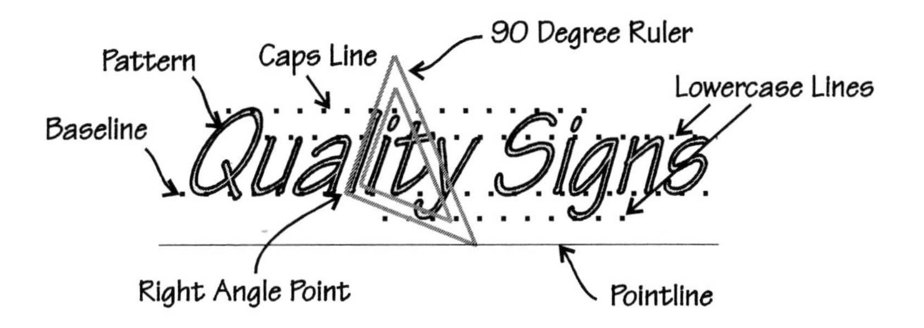

Stroke and Letter Spacing

With all letters the same size and pointing the same angle, focus on the design tube width. Draw the letter or design stroke as close to tube size as possible. An impeccable design with too large a tube stroke will create problems. Too wide a stroke makes it easy to bend within pattern lines; however, the glass tube letter spacing will vary and look haphazard. The closer the design is drawn to the desired tube diameter, the better chance the finished product will resemble the original design.

Correct letter spacing is important to legibility. Often, letters need tweaking to better readability. Use a basic rule of design and flip the pattern upside down. Step back and visually compare the area between letters. These areas should appear equal in space but not be equal since correct letter spacing is not mathematical.

If a letter looks out of balance, trace it on a small piece of paper, nudge it a little and tape into place. Flip the pattern upside down, step back and compare spacing again. When it looks right, tape or trace the letter permanently in place. Proper letter spacing requires a keen eye.

Identify Straight Areas

Identify straight areas on the pattern by laying a straight tube along straight lines. Where the pattern pulls away from the tube is where the curve begins and a straight area ends. Mark the pattern at these change points to make measuring more accurate. When using a blowhose to measure, simply run the hose from the end of a straight area through to the curve end. This helps determine the proper length of tubing required to form the bend.

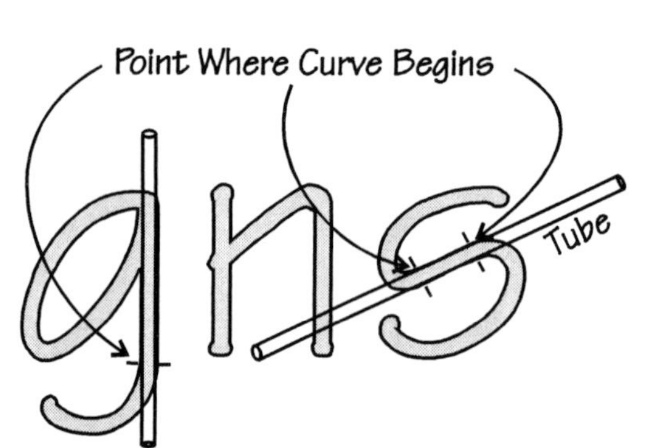

Figure 7-4
Identifying straight areas

Line Extensions

Line extensions help align bends quickly and accurately, tangent to a curve. To make a line extension, align a straight tube tangent to the end of a curve. Draw dashed or colored lines tightly around the tube. Aligning a tube with the line extension after forming a curve assures proper tube position. Keeping straight tubes tangent to the curve on the pattern helps to form smoother glass curves.

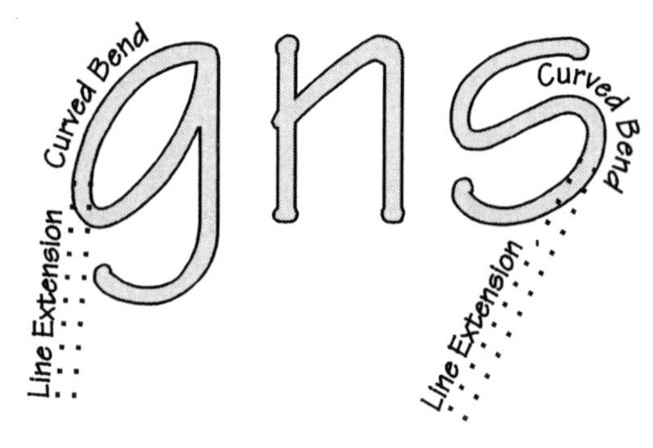

Figure 7-5
Line extensions

Mapping the Pattern

Some craftsmen begin bending without a plan. They figure how a letter or design is best bent while working. However, by mentally bending the sign in its entirety before bending the glass, one finds improved ways of working. Often planning leads to fewer welds, less blockout and sometimes less tubing being used. Most importantly, a fully mapped pattern frees the craftsman to concentrate on the quality of a bend–you are not thinking about the next maneuver, since it is already marked for you. Any system of mapping will work.

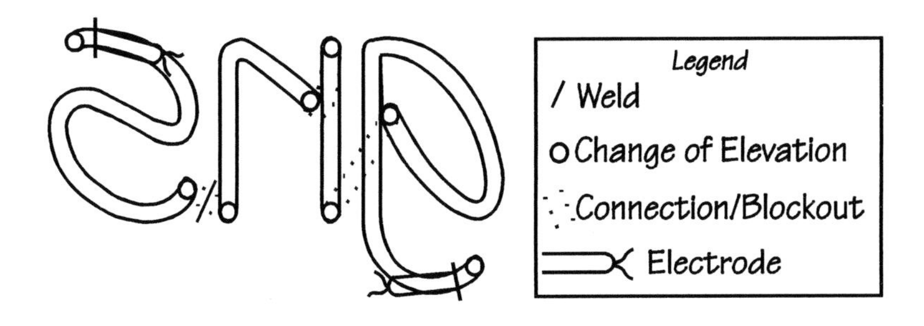

Figure 7-6 Basic pattern mapping

Exercises

Objective To become accustom with skills used to make basic neon designs and patterns.

Discussion Creating a workable pattern from a worthwhile design requires skill and practice. Some find it easier to hire someone else to do the job. Discover whether you have natural skills to make quality neon patterns.

Procedure Create simple sign designs on a computer, if you have access to one. If you do not, use or trace a simple design from the phone book or a business card. Enlarge it using a projector or copier, clean up the design, reverse then map the pattern for bending.

Helpful Hints for Making Patterns

1. Begin with simple block letters then advance to script and fancier letter styles or designs.
2. Use an erasable pencil on inexpensive paper found at sign or art supply stores. Butcher paper is sometimes used to make patterns.
3. Use a compass to draw round circles. A large, inexpensive compass can be purchased at art supply stores.
4. Use french curves to aid drawing irregular curves. Draw freehand curves from the inside. This is more natural than drawing from outside the curve.
5. Use a light table to reverse an image. The light shines through the paper pattern making it easy to transfer the image to bending pattern

material or to the paper backside. Or, simply trace over the design with a marker so the ink soaks through the paper to the backside. Large sheets of carbon paper also are used to reverse patterns but are messy.

Figure 7-7 Do-it-yourself light table

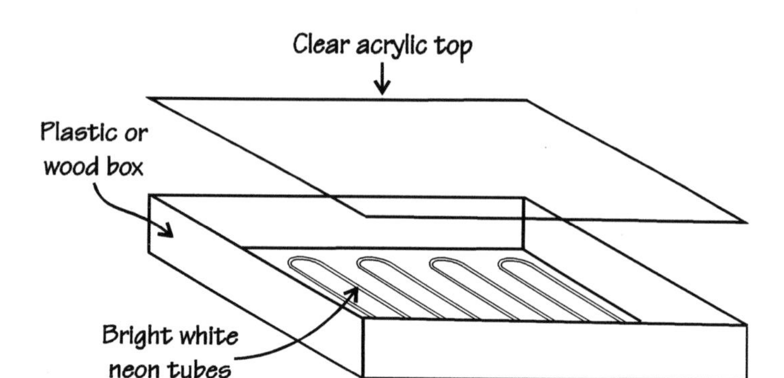

6. On multiunit jobs, label individual units both on the pattern and on the finished tube. This helps glassblower and installer keep track of each tube during manufacture and installation. Common labeling formats are An to Znn and AAn to ZZnn where n is a number.
7. Use multiple patterns and basic tools when mass-producing a sign. This increases production by allowing work to continue while a bend cools and by minimizing flame adjustments.
8. Use brass or stainless steel screen over a reversed paper pattern. These screens remain flat even after extensive use.

CHAPTER

8

Bending Script Letters

There are many script, also called cursive, letter styles and methods for bending them. This chapter establishes some basic rules and guidelines to aid mapping and bending script letters in neon.

Mapping a Script Pattern

Script letters are mostly made of small and large curves. So knowing where one curve begins and another ends helps to determine the length of tubing needed to form a bend. To determine separate ribbon fire bends on a script letter, divide shallow curves from sharp ones–separate small U-shapes from large U-shapes. Identify them by making marks on the pattern. Please see Figure 8-1.

Planning Ahead

Once curves are separated, mentally bend glass to the pattern then completely map the pattern. Before actually bending glass, however, consider the basic rules for bending letters: (1) If there is an inside to a letter, bend it first. (2) If there is a ribbon fire curve that helps form the inside, make it first.

Remembering and following these two rules help when bending a script letter that has two or more interior sections. Careful planning will help avoid overlapping tubes making the task simpler.

When bending script, it is common to bend out of sequence. Which bends are made first, is determined by careful planning. Usually, it is best to save a basic bend or small ribbon fire curve out of sequence. This saved bend is used to fold the completed letter sections together.

Bending Smooth Script

Creating smooth script requires much bending experience. Nevertheless, one aid to create smooth curves is to heat into the previous ribbon bend an inch or two. The transition point between the first and second heat resists softening, so positioning it deeper into the flame assures better heating since ribbon burner ends seldom heat evenly.

Before adjusting a curve to the pattern, anchor all previous bends in position. It is easy to be over involved handling molten tubing only to realize too late that previous bends were out of position. As bending continues, more bends are incorrectly positioned and the glass fits the pattern in few spots. It only takes a moment to situate and anchor previous bends then adjust the molten tubing to the neon pattern.

Figure 8-1
Separating curves

Forming Multiple Curves by Preheating

It is possible to form several small curves at once by preheating a section of tubing. The technique works best with letters five inches or less in height and small tube diameters. Any sharp curve surrounded by shallow curves is a good candidate for using the preheating technique.

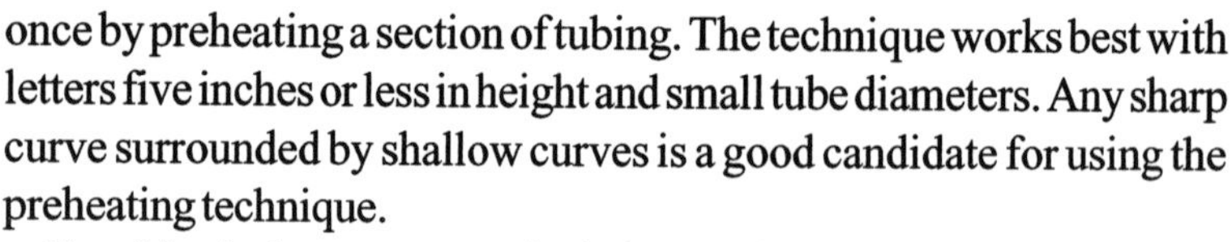

Consider the lower case, script letter E. The sharpest part of the letter is bordered by two shallow curves. By preheating the sharp curve for several seconds, it will bend more during formation than the surrounding shallow curves. This helps form the three curves simultaneously.

A preheat is made by passing the preheat area through a flame six to ten times. The amount of preheating, depends on the severity of the difference between the curves, sharper curves require more heat. After preheating the area, the entire length is heated in a ribbon burner, both shallow curves and sharp.

During heating, pay particular attention to the tubing on either side of the preheat. It is easy to leave the fire before these lengths are molten since the preheated area creates a false sense of fluidity. The entire length must be fluid, both shallow curves and sharp. Once this length is molten, form the bend in-line with gravity by looping the tubes or by crossing over. Then quickly puff air into the tube to assure even tube diameter. At the table, take care that molten tubing does not stick to other parts of the glass or strain will develop.

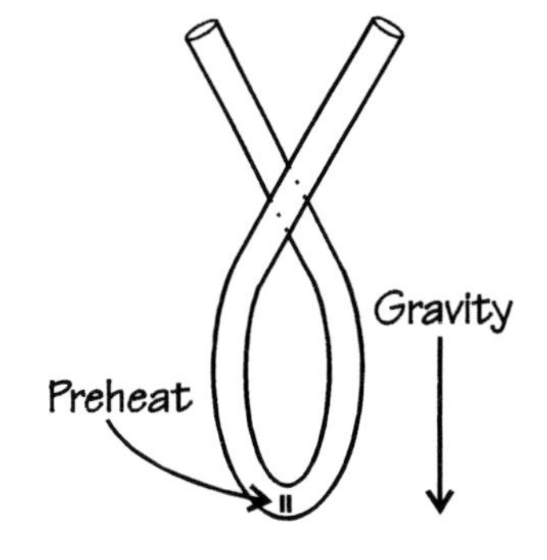

Figure 8-2
Forming multiple curves by preheating.

Lettering Layout

The following illustrations offer bend-by-number sequence for making script letters. Not all letters are shown as most are derived from these and previous examples. Since one script letter usually flows into the next, little blockout is used between them. As such, commercial style bending, leaving visibly lit tubes off the table, is generally acceptable so long as the finished tube is not dipped into blockout. Dipping a commercial style unit in blockout paint coats all elevated tubes. This results in painting out tubes meant to be lighted.

Only one type of script lettering style is shown here. Nevertheless, the bending sequence and methodology used to derive the sequence is usable in forming other script style letters too.

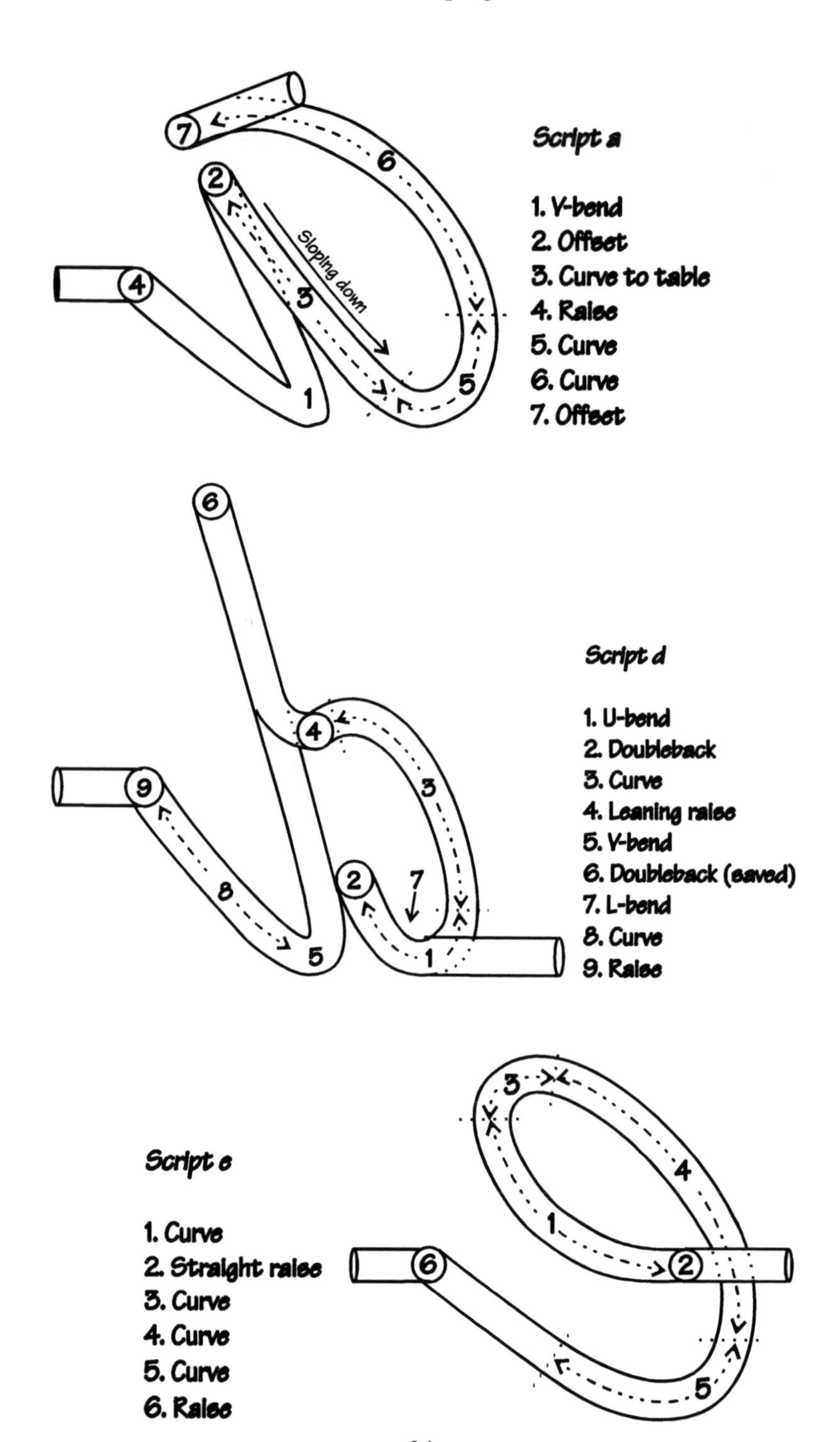
7
6
2
Sloping down
4
3
5
1
Script a
1. V-bend
2. Offset
3. Curve to table
4. Raise
5. Curve
6. Curve
7. Offset
6
Script d
1. U-bend
2. Doubleback
3. Curve
4. Leaning raise
5. V-bend
6. Doubleback (saved)
7. L-bend
8. Curve
9. Raise
4
9
3
8
2
7
5
1
3
Script e
1. Curve
2. Straight raise
3. Curve
4. Curve
5. Curve
6. Raise
4
1
6
2
5

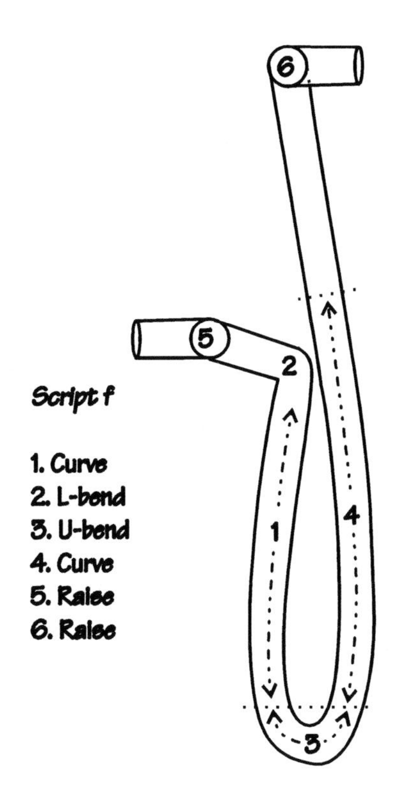

Script f

1. Curve
2. L-bend
3. U-bend
4. Curve
5. Raise
6. Raise

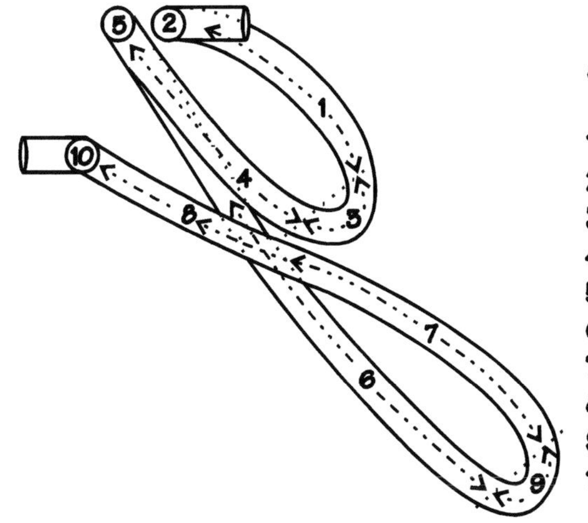

Script g

1. Curve
2. Offset
3. U-bend
4. Curve onto block
5. Doubleback
6. Curve
7. Curve on to block
8. Curve down to table
9. U-bend (fold)
10. Raise

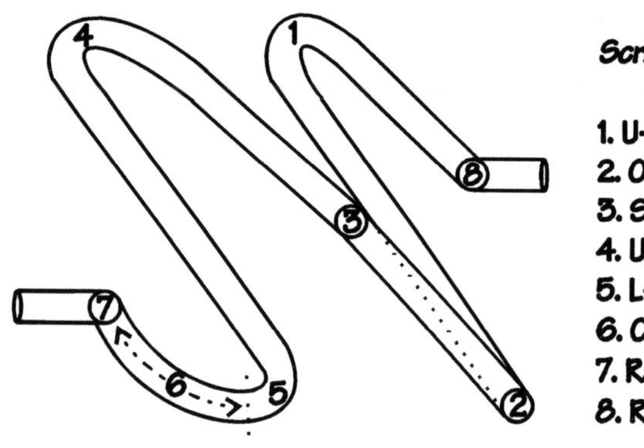

Script n

1. U-bend
2. Offset
3. Straight Drop
4. U-bend
5. L-bend (rounded)
6. Curve
7. Raise
8. Raise

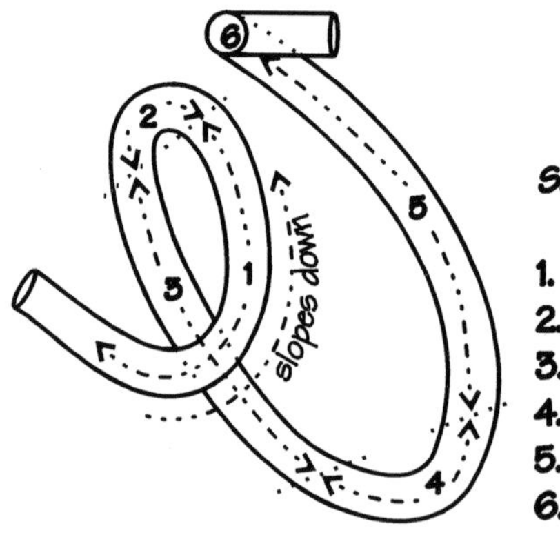

Script o

1. Curve (sloping)
2. U-bend
3. Curve
4. Curve
5. Curve
6. Offset

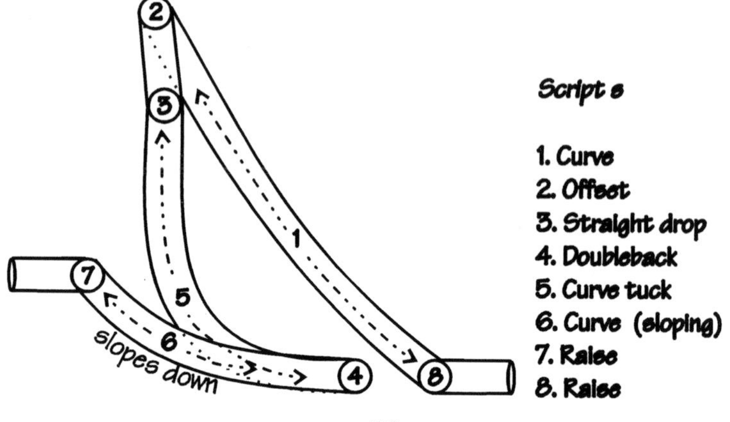

Script s

1. Curve
2. Offset
3. Straight drop
4. Doubleback
5. Curve tuck
6. Curve (sloping)
7. Raise
8. Raise

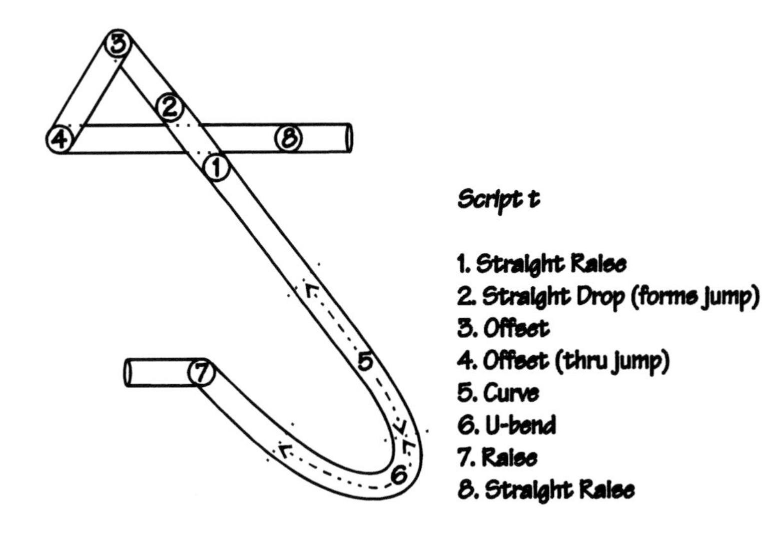

Exercises

Objective To develop basic script letter bending skills and gain further experience using the ribbon burner.

Discussion There are many ways to bend script letters. Certain conventions exist to make bending script letters easier, more logical.

Procedure Make usable script patterns by tracing and expanding the provided images or create your own design. Practice the suggested bending variations for each letter then try developing your own workable sequence. Use ten or twelve millimeter clear tubing to begin then advance to large diameter tubes and coated tubes.

Helpful Hints for Bending Script Letters

1. Properly adjust all flames. Clear the table of unnecessary items.
2. Keep the appropriate size and number of glass blowing tools nearby.
3. Rotate the pattern to best facilitate positioning a bend.
4. Align bends with gravity and split forces between both hands.
5. Anchor previous bends before adjusting subsequent bends.
6. On large curves, understand tangency and where it is applied. For more information, see Chapter Nine.
7. Heat one or more inches back into a previous curve.

8. Consider preheating to form multiple curves in one motion.
9. Blow out small, sharp turns and large diameter tubes.
10. Consider using the crossor cannon fire instead of the ribbon burner to form very small curves.
11. Some bending positions require passing a hand over a burner flame. Make this move quickly to avoid burns. Before attempting such a maneuver, consider other positions since often-alternative motions are simpler.
12. Make extra marks on a coated tube opposite the regular marks. This makes it easy to keep the area centered in the flame when rotating the tube. Make these marks lighter to lessen chance of confusion.
13. Compare your practice letters with those found in the field.
14. Relax.

Ribbon Burner Tip

If the ribbon burner does not heat evenly to the ends, break heating time into halves on opposite sides of the burner. Make one-half the heat on one side the burner then immediately finish heating the tube on the opposite side of the burner. Or halfway through heating, carefully switch the tube ends in your hands to aid more uniform heating.

CHAPTER 9

Large Circles and Border Tubes

The human eye is sensitive to variations in curves and detects even slight wobbles. Hence, bending smooth large circles is difficult even for seasoned craftsman. Some basic guidelines help apprentice craftsman learn to create reasonably smooth circles with dedicated practice.

Border tubes ordinarily are long straight tubes with bends only near electrodes. Keeping welded lengths visually straight with electrodes positioned correctly for installation can be challenging. The following guidelines help to form smooth curves and straight border tubes.

The Large Circle Pattern

To form a smooth large circle in glass, begin with a near perfect pattern. A poorly drawn pattern results in distorted curves and flat spots. So, use a computer or a large compass to draw an accurate circle. Art supply stores offer inexpensive compasses in many sizes.

Understanding Tangency

Understanding tangency helps to form smooth curves. Imagine a speeding car rounding a turn. The car is traveling too fast to stay on the path and suddenly leaves the road traveling in a straight line. While the car remained on the road, it followed a series of points tangent to the path. When the car left the road, its direction of travel straightened and it no longer shared common points with the curve, it was no longer tangent to the curve.

The tube path also must remain tangent to the curve. Straight unheated tubing should leave a curved pattern straight away, like a speeding car. Unbent tubing should run outside the curved pattern, never across or inside it. Incorrectly bent curves require reheating then bending away from the arch. This can result in wobbles or flat spots because the tube is first bent with the path then away.

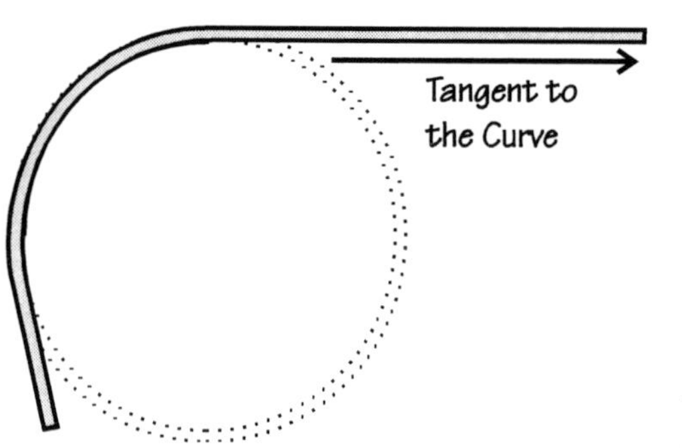

Figure 9-1 Tangency

Smile or Frown?

Before bending a large circle, discover whether it is easier to form a smile or frown. Many discover that bending away from themselves (a smile) is easier than bending toward themselves (a frown). Try both ways to discover which method works best for you then practice diligently.

Working with Gravity, Transition Point and Bending

Normally, you heat a tube length to molten and let gravity form a curve less than that on the pattern. Then you bend the glass to tangency directly onto the pattern. Yet when bending very large circles, it is easy to heat a tube so gravity causes the glass to exceed the curve on the pattern, less heat would cause strain. Here, it helps to pull gently outwards on the molten tube to lessen the curve while heating. A slight pull does not appreciably stretch the glass but it does remove some curve caused by gravity.

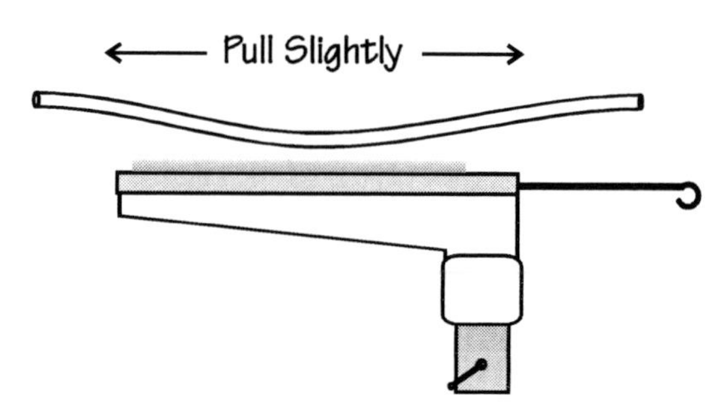

Figure 9-2 Pulling to diminish excess curve

The place on a bent tube where one curve meet another is called the transition point, where one bend transitions to another. Because the transition point heats more slowly than previously unheated tubing and since the ribbon burner flame is not as hot near the ends as the middle, it helps to heat one or two inches back into the previous curve. Positioning the transition point deeper into the flame helps heat it faster and more evenly.

To further aid forming smooth curves, position prior bends on the pattern first, then bring molten tubing into place. Or, try moving prior bends and molten tubing into place simultaneously, splitting bending forces. Either method is valid. Also, let a bend cool a minute or more before forming adjacent bends. This lessens chance of strain and aids control by maintaining an even temperature gradient across the tube. Work on another part of the circle while heated tubes cool.

Border Tubes

Border tubes ordinarily are long, straight tubes lighting the border of a window, room or building exterior. Forming straight welded lengths of tubing is a challenge for most beginning craftsman. But it is border tube ends that matter most during installation so special attention required.

Electrode Penetrations

Most border tube installations require each border end have an electrode placed into a receptacle or housing at a right angle. The length from electrode tip to border tube edge is called the penetration and this length varies from job to job. The installer determines the penetration during initial planning. See Electrode Housing and Penetration in Figure 9-3 and in Chapter Ten.

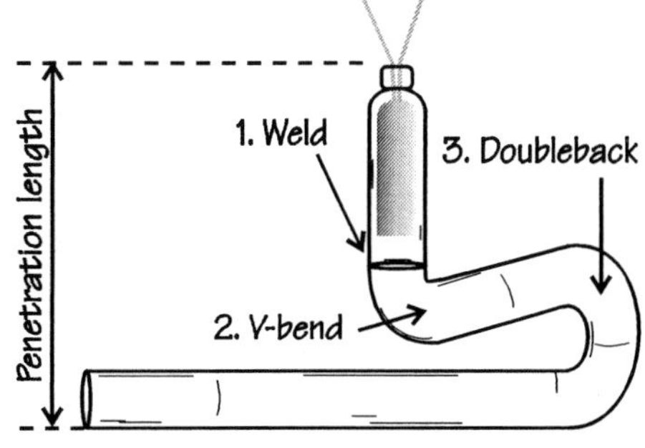

Figure 9-3 V-bend Doubleback penetration

V-bend Doubleback

Ordinarily, a penetrating electrode must be kept from a structure edge or obstruction yet allow the tube to be mounted closely to the wall. To provide these measures, a V-bend and Doubleback is often used. First, an electrode is welded on a tube end then a V-bend is made on or near the weld. Finally, the electrode and V-bend are doubled back so the electrode forms a ninety-degree angle to the border tube. This effectively insets the electrode from the structure edge or obstruction and allows the tube to be mounted close to the surface.

Double-Doubleback

To connect running border tube electrodes, the double-Doubleback is sometimes used. This method doubles back the tubes in one plane then doubles back the electrodes in another. The electrodes meet end to end and get covered with a straight, approved insulator. To better facilitate some installations, the electrode doublebacks are leaned at an angle over the border tubes. This effectively hides the electrodes and insulators on border tubes mounted high, overhead.

Figure 9-4 The double-Doubleback

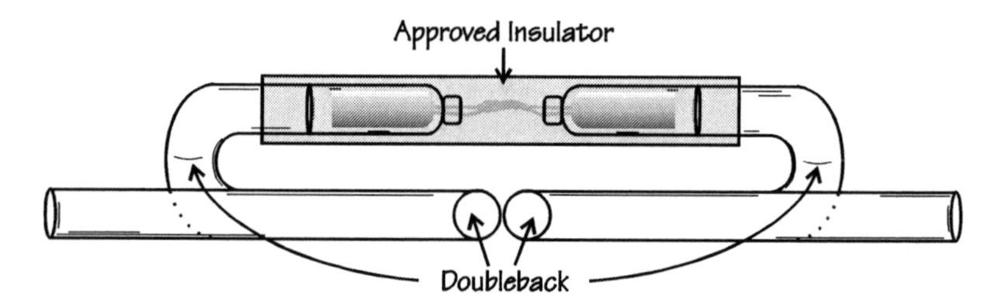

The Drop Behind

Another way to connect running border tubes is to use the drop behind. An electrode from one tube is closely doubled back. The electrode on the adjoining tube is dropped behind the doubled back electrode or angled slightly along side it. The two are connected and insulated in *three deep* fashion, three deep referring to three levels of tubing. An approved electrical insulator covers both electrodes.

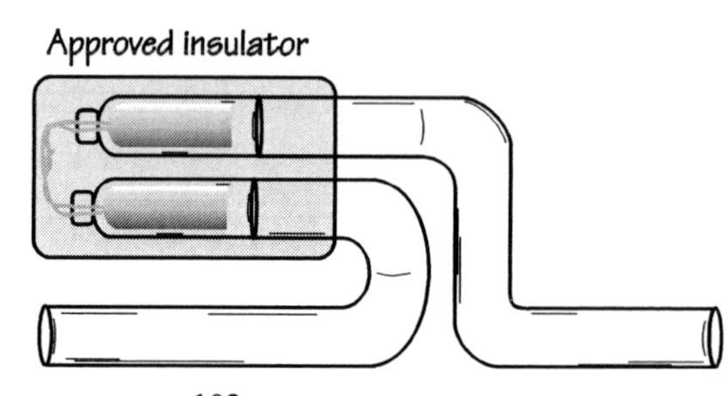

Figure 9-5 The drop behind

Jumpers

Border tube electrodes often are doubled back and

connected with high voltage jumper wire. An industry-accepted insulator, usually made of glass, covers the electrodes and a glass tube insulates the wire. In some jurisdictions, using high voltage jumper wires is not allowed. Always check with local officials before using jumper wires.

Welding Border Tubes

Border tube lengths vary, but six to ten foot long tubes are common. Welding long sections of tubing is cumbersome, so most craftsman use a tall block to elevate one tube end above a table. Then by hand, they angle the remaining tube to meet it. Elevating the tube ends leaves room to swing a handtorch underneath. When the weld is finished, the elevating block is removed and the molten, joined tubes sat flat on the table for straightening. The tube is aligned with a straightedge or with a line drawn on the table. Some just look down the tube to assure it is straight.

To simplify welding border tubes, make border tube sections in half then weld each half together. This keeps the work balanced, always joining halves. To make the job even easier, use a border tube jig.

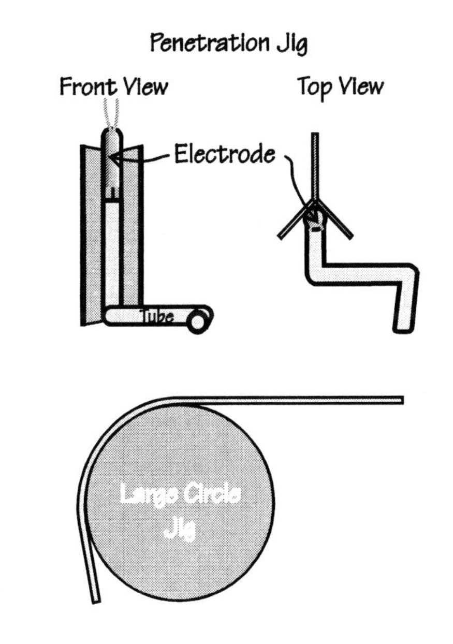

Figure 9-6
Common jigs

Exercises

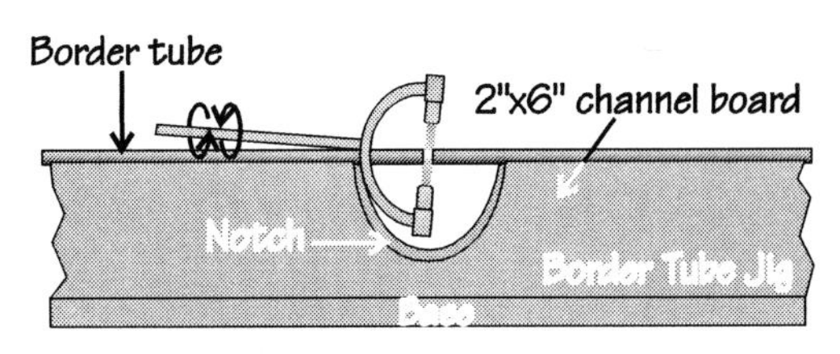

Objective To become familiar with manufacturing large curves and border tubes.

Discussion Bending a large circle has long been considered the test of a good neon craftsman. Equally challenging is working on the end of a full stick of tubing when making a border tube. So learning to make large circles and border tubes is a big step toward being recognized as a true craftsman.

Procedure Use a computer or large compass to draw two concentric circles about two and one-half and three feet in diameter. Bend each circle in twelve and fifteen millimeter clear tubing until satisfactory results develop. Compare practice work to work found in the market-place. Weld at least two circles together as shown in Figure 9-7.

Practice forming the different electrode ends used to connect border tubes. Practice welding and handling border tubes of varying length using described methods.

Figure 9-7 Two concentric circles

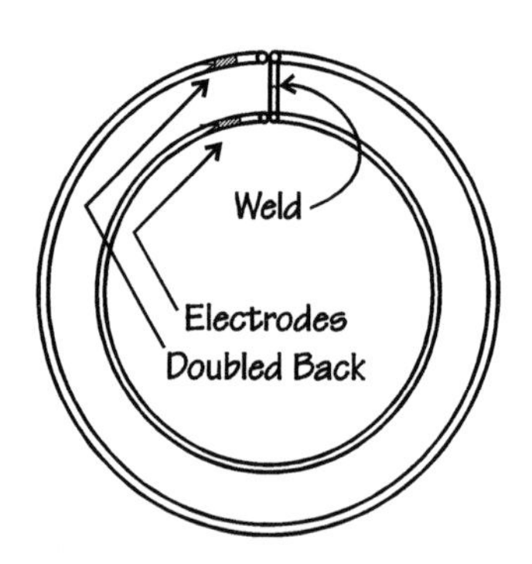

CHAPTER

10

Double Outline and Channel Letters

Some designs or letter styles are best represented in double tube or double outline. The typestyle either is too wide or complicated to represent with a single tube stroke. Double outline adds style and elegance to a sign and the additional light produced by the double tube attracts attention.

Double outline signs require much more tubing than do single tube units (see Table 14-3 in Chapter 14). So careful planning and consideration is given to total linear tube length. A unit made of too much linear tubing makes proper tube processing impossible. Handling and mounting are more difficult and larger or additional transformers are needed to light the extra glass. Double outline signs sometimes cost more to manufacture but often are easier to bend.

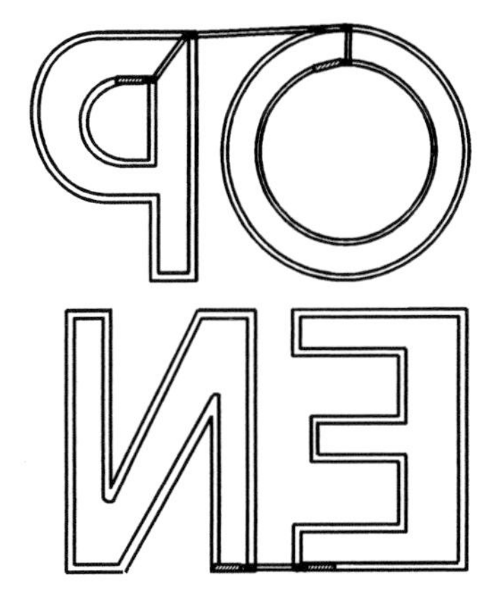

Figure 10-1 Double outline -block letters

Rule of Thumb

Basic bending rules still apply: begin bending the inside of a letter or design and start with a ribbon bend if it helps form the inside. Bending double outline often requires saving a bend for folding two segments of a letter or design together. Saving a bend allows the craftsman to move previous bends out of the way until another segment is completed. The saved bend is later used to fold the piece together.

Double Outline Script

Bending glass tubing to a double outline script pattern requires much planning. Sometimes more than one bend is saved out of sequence to fold the piece together. However, the following method also proves useful.

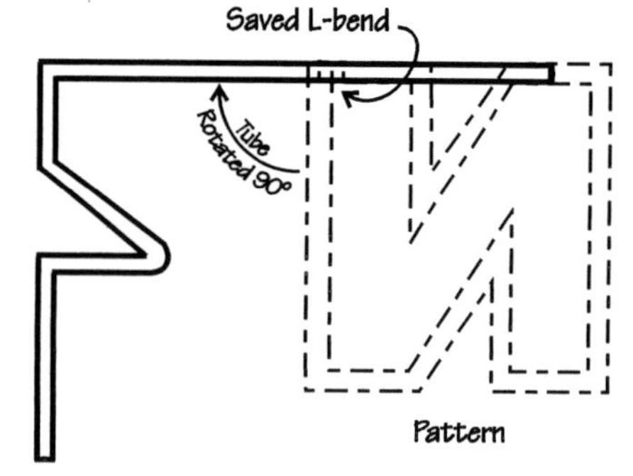

Figure 10-2 Saving a bend for folding

Horizontal Separation Method

Consider separating the sign horizontally across its center. This splits the sign into a top and a bottom half. Figure 10-3 represents a script window sign of such linear footage that the sign is divided into three separate units. This is to make processing and handling easier.

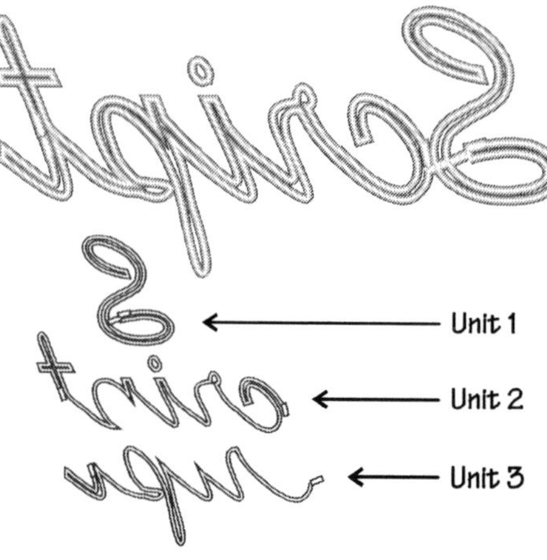

Figure 10-3 Horizontal separation method

The three units consist of the following: the S is one unit, the top half of CRIPT is a unit and the bottom half of CRIPT is another. Electrodes connect the S and C; another pair of electrodes connect separate halves of the T and will be wired together upon mounting. The remaining two electrodes, one on the S and the other on the C, connect to a transformer. Splitting this sign horizontally simplifies bending, tube processing and mounting.

Channel Letters

Channel letters are made of outline neon lettering. Ordinarily, they are individual letters outlined in single or double tube and sometimes consist of many strokes. Very large channel letters are made of dozens of neon units arranged in many outlines. Some are so large or complex they are lifted into place by crane or helicopter. Currently, channel letters are installed in nearly every strip mall in America.

Most channel letters are used to illuminate cut-to-shape acrylic letters. The neon tube resides in a *can* or *pan* made of sheet metal or plastic and is hidden behind a translucent, colored acrylic face. A face made of clear acrylic or a channel with no face is called "exposed" channel. Neon tubes used to backlight an opaque face are labeled "reverse" channel. For added effect, some signs make use of both exposed and reverse.

Figure 10-4 Exposed channel rendition (no face)

Exposed channel demands care when manufacturing. The tubes are forever visible so big variations from the pattern or unsmooth curves are noticeable. Other kinds of channel letters hide the tube. So most shops make production a priority over appearance; variations from the pattern of one full tube diameter are often acceptable. The variation must not interfere with installation, however.

Channel letters often are made of thirteen or fifteen millimeter clear or coated-white glass tubing. This is because the colors red and white illuminate best most colored acrylic faces. Exposed and reverse channel letters use any color tube, as the colored light is clearly visible, not altered by the acrylic.

Electrode Housing and Penetration

Like border tubes, channel letter electrodes are commonly bent ninety-degrees to the main tube. The length from the tube edge to the electrode tip is determined by the installation and is called penetration. See Figure 9-3 and figure 10-5.

When installed, electrodes are placed into glass or ceramic housings. The housing contains a spring that connects to a transformer high voltage lead. It is tube support length and electrode housing depths that determine penetration length. If penetration length is manufactured too short, the spring and electrode lead wires do not make contact leaving the unit inoperable. If penetration length is too long, the force of the housing spring or the housing end wall may break the unit.

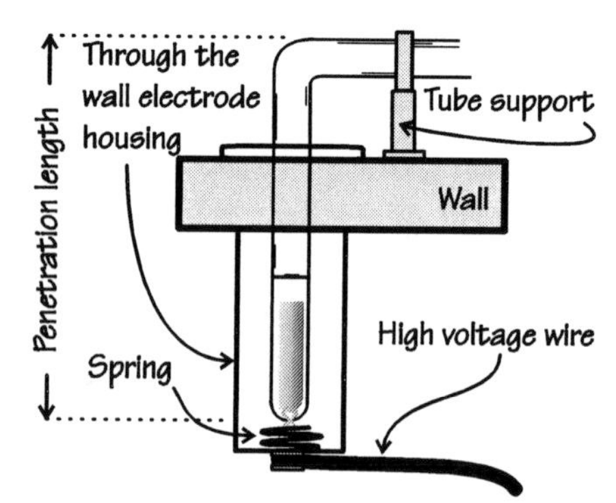

Figure 10-5
Electrode housing

Placing Electrodes Accurately

Proper electrode placement is essential when making channel letters. Pattern designers are careful to mark the exact electrode placement on a pattern using crosshairs. This is because the same pattern used to make the glass is used to manufacture all other components too. Most often, this placement ensures the installer does not run into problems while hanging the sign, problems like drilling or cutting into existing plumbing, wiring or other building structure. It makes the job easier if everyone hits the mark. For the tubebender, it does not matter how well the glass letters are bent if the electrodes do not fit the housings. The units most likely cannot be propery installed.

Like border tubes, L-bend Doubleback and V-bend Doubleback penetrations are made on channel letters too. To make the penetration easier to form, consider drawing a side pattern to scale showing the electrode, L- or V-bend and Doubleback.

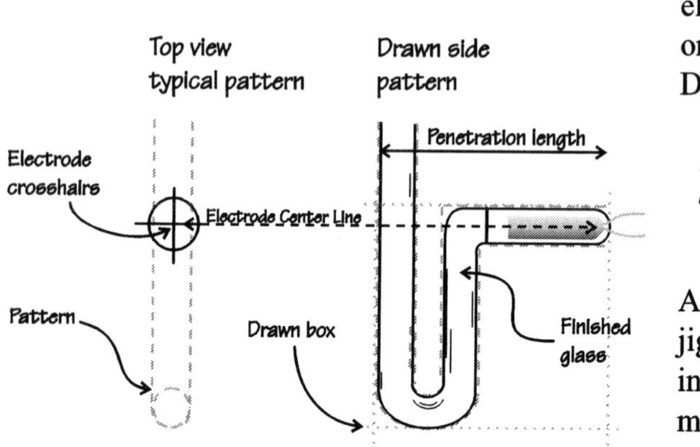

Figure 10-6
Side pattern bending

A penetration jig, as shown in Figure 9-6 may help too.

Exercises

Objective To become accustom to bending double outline designs.

Discussion Double outline is used to form shapely letter styles impossible to represent in single stroke format. Double and multiple outline also is used to illuminate acrylic covered neon mounted in a formed *can* called a channel letter.

Procedure Practice bending double outline window signs using the following designs or those of your choosing. Use an opaque projector or other method to enlarge the designs then map to make useful patterns. Tube the pattern as shown in Figure 10-7.

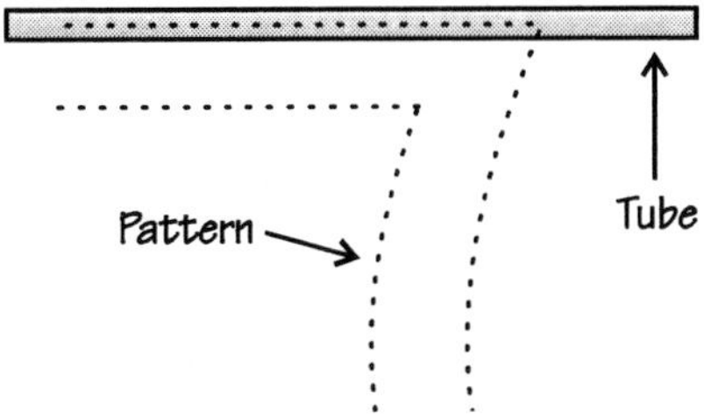

Pattern
Tube

Figure 10-7 Tubing a double outline pattern

Draw any large, double outline letter and practice bending as a channel letter in fifteen millimeter tubing. Try to keep individual unit length between ten and fifteen linear feet of tubing. Most channel letters are easier to bend, process and install this way.

Tips and Hints

1. When bending large, multiunit double outline signs consider using the horizontal separation method to ease the task.
2. Channel Letters regularly house unexposed neon tubes so near perfect bends are not necessary. Try bending two L-bends at once by preheating the center points of two close L-bends. Alternately heat each point several seconds in a crossor cannon fire. Then rotate over the ribbon burner the entire marked length of tubing.

Once the L-bend center points are molten, hold the tube over the flame in the ready position a few more seconds. Remove the tube and bend. Blow out the bends and position them on the pattern.

When performed correctly, the preheated areas form two slightly rounded but useable L-bends. The tubing between the L-bends does not become molten and remains straight. This method is used to speed channel letter bending.

3. Compare your work with that found in double outline window signs and exposed channel letter signs.

Figure 10-8
Double outline practice patterns

CHAPTER

11

Electrodes and Tube Processing

Tubulated and Non-tubulated Electrodes

Electrodes are electrical current carrying devices designed to ionize inert gas to luminous levels. To a large degree, they determine the life of a tube. All standard electrodes consist of lead-in wires, a metal electrode shell and glass jacket. They are manufactured either tubulated or non-tubulated. The tubulated electrode incorporates a small diameter tube used to evacuate and gas a unit during processing. In some instances, only non-tubulated electrodes are used. Then the unit is tubulated somewhere between the electrodes, ordinarily near the unit center, for evacuating and gassing.

Lead-in Wires

Lead-in wires carry electrical current from a neon transformer to the electrode shell. Three piece lead-in wires are made of nickel, a copper clad wire and a piece of stranded nickel or iron that is attached to the electrode shell. The copper clad section allows superior metal to glass bond at the pinch seal. It expands and contracts with heat at or near the rate of soft glass ensuring a strain free, vacuum tight seal.

Metal Shell, Emitter Coating & Sputtering

The modern electrode metal shell is a result of trial, error and experimentation. It is made of highly pure, plated steel and covered with an emission coating blended by the manufacturer for easy processing and long tube life. Electrode shells are designed to last hundreds of thousands of hours.

During bombarding high voltage electric current creates heavy, positively charged atoms called cations (cat~ions). These particles are forcibly drawn to the electrode developing sufficient momentum to pulverize the electrode shell. The term describing this destruction is "sputtering." An emitter coating on the shell releases electrons during bombardment. Electrons given off by the emitter coating travel through the tube neutralizing cations lessening damage thereby minimizing sputtering.

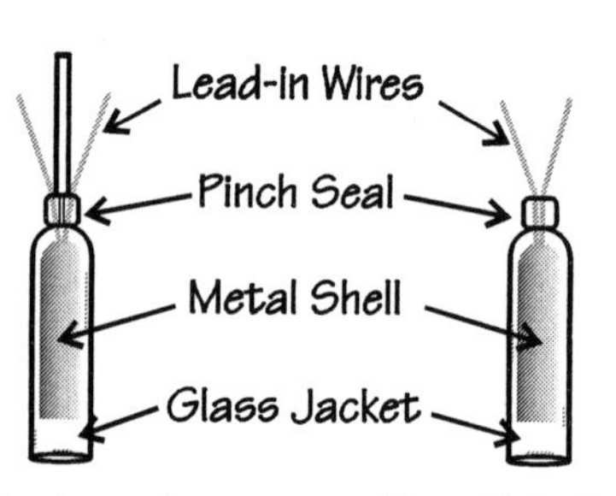

Figure 11-1
Typical electrode

Not all impurities are removed during processing so the emitter coating converts to a chemical getter. This action cleans up most residual impurities during aging or tube burn-in.

Electrode shells incompletely processed or converted during bombarding remain covered with emitter coating. The coating releases impurities into a finished tube causing unfavorable color change even shortening tube life. This discoloration ordinarily finds its way to the tube center by virtue of molecular mass and electrical wave action. In mercury units, these impurities may combine with mercury causing visible dark stains. Hence, the importance of following electrode manufacturer directions for electrical current, vacuum and temperature to process completely the electrode shell during tube processing.

Glass Jacket, Mica, Ceramic Collar and Ratings

The electrode glass jacket is made of lead glass like neon tubing. This is so the two glasses bond when welded. The glass jacket is closed at the pinch seal and open to the tube opposite the pinch seal.

Some electrode manufacturers use a very thin sheet of mica rolled around the shell. This keeps the shell from contacting the glass jacket during processing that would crack or melt it. When welding the electrode to a tube, push the mica back from the splice if needed. Otherwise, the mica will interfere with the weld and cause glass strain.

The white ring at some electrode shell's open end is made of ceramic.

This collar provides extra protection from sputtering by breaking the momentum of heavy cations. It also aids to "center-fire" the electrode, more electrons produce light from the shell interior rather than the shell surface or ends. This way, many cations are drawn into the shell interior by electromotive force. Here, when sputtering occurs, metal knocked off the interior shell surface has good chance of redepositing on the shell interior rather than exiting into the tube. Exiting metal atoms shorten tube life by trapping inert gas atoms against the tube wall. This lowers tube pressure over time, unfavorably altering electrical properties.

Electrodes are rated in milliamperes, the amount of electric current they are designed to operate. Most electrodes are rated between twenty and eighty milliamperes. Low rated electrodes are used on small signs with low current transformers. High rated electrodes are used with large diameter tubes and high current transformers since large diameter tubes appear dim, the high current brightens them.

Tube Processing

Moisture from heating and cooling and minute pieces of cork or connector gets trapped in a tube during manufacture. Tube processing, or bombarding and pumping, is a method used to remove these impurities from a finished glass unit.

A few shops rinse finished tubes with either water or an acid solution to help remove impurities before bombardment. However, tap water contains bacteria and metals that add to tube contamination. Distilled water is best used as a rinse. The tube needs to be blown dry with low pressure, dry air before bombarding to remove residual moisture.

Bombarding and Equipment

Internal electrical bombardment is a process used to heat a finished tube to about four hundred twenty-five degrees Fahrenheit. The electrodes are then heated about sixteen hundred degrees Fahrenheit to process the electrode shell coating. After bombarding, high vacuum pumping removes the hot, impure vapors from the tube. Impurities left in a finished tube can cause one or more of the following problems: poor light output, discoloration, mercury stains, snaking or shortened tube life. Bombarding and pumping literally control what is considered the health and life of a tube.

Simple internal bombarding systems consist of a bombarding transformer, a variable electric choke, a magnetic switch and a manual "dead man" switch.

Bombarding Transformer and Jacob's ladder

Bombarding transformers are rated by electrical size. The rating term is kilovolt amps or "Kva". It is derived from the primary current multiplied by the primary voltage divided by one thousand. Most bombarding transformers are rated between five and twenty Kva. A larger rating indicates a more powerful bombarder.

A bombarding transformer operates at high voltage and danger of *electrocution* is very real. A Jacob's Ladder usually is installed as a safety measure. It is two, number four, bare, solid copper wires originating at the high voltage terminals. The wires curve toward one another then away with a gap about one-quarter to one-half inch between them. Should a neon unit break or a high voltage wire disconnect during bombarding, the Jacob's Ladder will shunt the electric current between the wires. Without this alternate path, electricity seeks ground by leaping to another less desirable point, like the operator or equipment. Mount a bombarder well away from the operator.

Figure 11-2 Choke, bombarding transformer (center) and switch (Daco Neon Equipment)

Choke Coil

In electrical conjunction with the bombarding transformer is the variable choke coil or "choke" as it is commonly referred. The choke function is to regulate electric current to the neon unit during bombarding. Without the ability to regulate current properly, it is possible the electrode emitter coating never is activated or it is burned off the electrode shell too. Variations of the choke exist but all regulate secondary current.

Other mechanical devices contribute to safe and efficient bombarding: a manual switch that turns off the primary circuit; a "dead man" switch to activate intermittently the bombarding transformer; and the magnetic switch to isolate the operator from primary voltage and secondary high voltage flashback should it occur.

Bombarding Station Setup

When setting up a bombarding station, it is practical to mount the dead man switch close to the choke since they are operated together. The vacuum, or main, stopcock also should be comfortably within reach. Minute adjustments to pressure levels within the tube assure proper tube and electrode processing. Though electrically grounded and equipped with a Jacob's Ladder, a bombarding transformer is potentially *life threatening*. Mount it well away from the operator or behind a suitably grounded or insulated barrier. Several inches of air space between the transformer and any surroundings also are preferred. Check with the manufacturer for proper installation of any bombarding equipment.

Figure 11-3 Schematic of a typical bombarding station

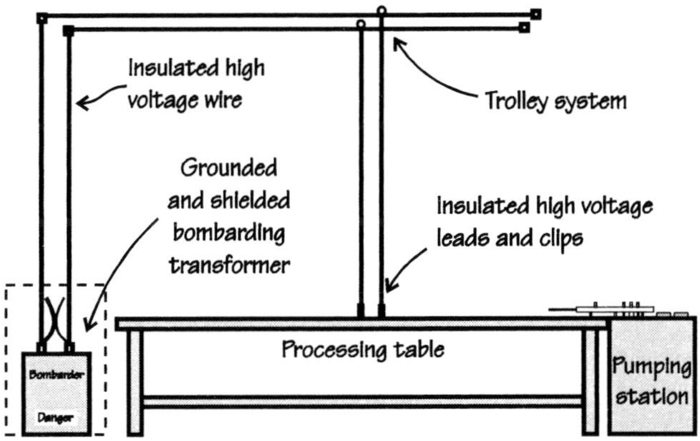

Many shops run high voltage wires from the bombarder to bare copper trolley wires. Trolley wires are mounted, but electrically isolated, on the ceiling or from a suitable wood frame. The bombarding current is transferred from the bombarder to the neon unit below through the trolley and insulated high voltage wire and clips.

Some mount the bombarder on, along side or under the tube processing table. They run high voltage wires from the transformer, across the table to the neon unit. Whatever the method, the goal is to transfer safely, yet conveniently high voltage electric current from the transformer to the neon unit.

The bombarding table is built of wood since a metal table is an electrical hazard. Make the table long–ten or twelve feet long. This makes processing border tubes or large letters convenient. The table should be about three feet wide, wide enough to process two tubes simultaneously side-by-side. A table too wide or too tall makes connecting and disconnecting units difficult. A standard wall outlet nearby for operating the spark coil.

Bombarding Ammeter

The bombarding ammeter is wired in electrical series between the bombarder and the tube to be processed. It displays the amount of electric current supplied to the unit during bombarding. The choke regulates the amount of current being delivered to the sign. A meter calibrated from zero ampere to one ampere or equivalently zero milliamperes to one thousand milliamperes is best since processing current usually is maintained between one hundred and six hundred milliamperes.

The ammeter also indicates possible electrical blow-through. Electricity passing through glass bends placed close together creates an electric potential difference that can blow through the glass tubing. Before processing, mica is placed between bends to discourage this from happening. Yet, if the electrical potential is great enough, electricity will blow through both mica and tubing. Before such an event, the ammeter needle shakes or rises then drops significantly as the potential difference develops. Increasing the vacuum in the tube decreases chance of blow through by lowering electrical resistance in the tube.

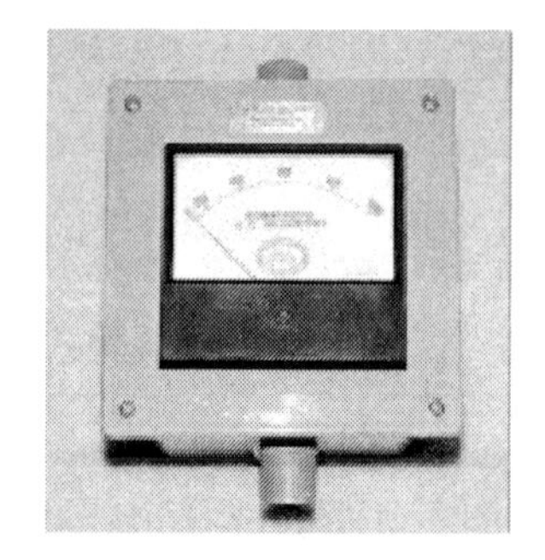

Figure 11-4 Bombarding ammeter
(Daco Neon Equipment)

Vacuum Equipment

A typical vacuum system includes a two stage vacuum pump capable of quickly creating and maintaining vacuum around one micron, and a manifold enabling the operator full control over vacuum and delivery of inert gases. A more sophisticated system might incorporate a glass or metal diffusion pump and a vacuum gauge.

Vacuum Pump

Most single stage pumps create vacuum in the twenty-five micron range, not suitable for use in luminous tube manufacture. However, a two stage pump can produce and maintain a deep vacuum. Many are factory tested to one-tenth of a micron though they do not produce this under normal shop conditions. Nevertheless, vacuum measured at the manifold of less than five microns is acceptable and contributes to a long lived tube. Two stage vacuum pumps are manufactured in several forms: belt drive, direct drive and turbo molecular. They are available from sign supplers, scientific supply stores and other vacuum related industry.

Figure 11-5 Direct drive two-stage vacuum pump (Edwards High Vacuum Int'l. from SPI Supplies www.2spi.com)

Glass and Metal Manifolds

The manifold is made of glass or metal and uses a bank of stopcocks, also made of glass or metal, to give the operator control of vacuum, noble gas and air pressure within the manifold and neon unit.

A glass manifold is made of lead, soda or borosilicate tubing. However, neon tubing does not seal to borosilicate glass so an adapter allowing the connection is usually supplied. Glass manifolds are available with grease or greaseless stopcocks. Greaseless stopcocks cost more but require much less care.

A metal manifold usually is made of stainless steel. Because it is made of metal, care is exercised to protect the user from high voltage hazard. The inability to see inside the manifold makes it difficult to determine cleaning schedules and the spark coil cannot be used to locate a manifold leak. For these reasons, the glass manifold is generally preferred.

Figure 11-6 Greaseless borosilicate vacuum manifold
(Transco)

Diffusion Pump

The diffusion pump is made of borosilicate glass or stainless steel. It requires use of a "backing pump" since it does not function above one hundred microns pressure. Combination mechanical pump and diffusion pumps are available from scientific and sign equipment suppliers.

The diffusion pump is air or water cooled since maintaining proper operating temperature is important to the pump function. The pump uses a silicone-based fluid in its operation. The fluid is heated to boiling under vacuum during rough pumping. Upon boiling, the fluid expands creating a partial vacuum on one side of the pump. When the fluid cools, it condenses lessening its volume again contributing to the creation of vacuum.

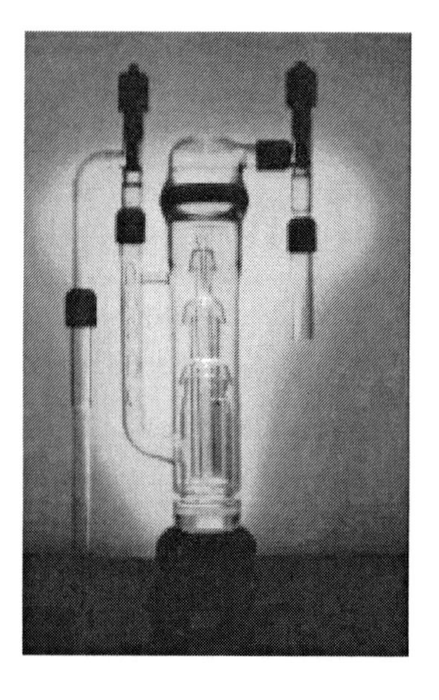

Figure 11-7 Glass diffusion pump
(Mike Wheeler Custom Glass Blowing Chandler, AZ.)

If the fluid is heated too high, it reduces pump efficiency and can drive pumping fluid into the rest of the vacuum system. Too low a fluid temperature renders the pump ineffective as too little vapor pressure is maintained to contribute to quality vacuum creation.

The diffusion pump's biggest advantage is its tremendous pumping speed reaching capacities of six hundred liters per minute and more. Since it is important to remove impurities quickly from a tube while they are hot, high in kinetic energy, a diffusion pump assures the best chance for their removal. This results in more impurities being removed from the tube increasing overall tube quality. The diffusion pump is capable of generating deep vacuum about one and one hundredth micron or better.

It is argued whether adding a diffusion pump is necessary to produce quality neon tubes; some shops do well without one. Indeed, a poorly maintained diffusion pump or one not properly operated decreases tube quality. Still, many shops swear by them.

The life and efficiency of any pump depends upon cleanliness. As such, clean the pump periodically and change the operating fluid regularly as directed by the manufacturer.

Vacuum and Pressure Gauges

A vacuum or pressure gauge is used to determine relative pressure within the manifold and neon unit. It also can indicate a leaking stopcock or weld, ultimate vacuum and backfill pressure.

Figure 11-8 Digital vacuum gauge (Daco Neon Equipment)

Two types of vacuum gauge are commonly used in the neon trade. One is a good indicator of rough vacuum, zero to thirty millimeters of mercury or equivalently zero to thirty Torr. The other is an indicator of high vacuum from one hundred microns down to one micron or equivalently, one milli-Torr. Ordinarily, the high vacuum gauge is not used for indicating backfill pressure as this measure is beyond gauge range. The rough gauge or butyl gauge is used instead.

Rough Vacuum

The rough vacuum gauge is either the Bourdon capsule or the Aneroid barometer type. It is used primarily for indicating initial, rough vacuum and filling pressure. In operation, an internal mechanical component is exposed to a changing pressure that curves or straightens a delicate tube or flexible chamber to which a pointer is connected. The pointer indicates vacuum on a numbered dial, usually in millimeters of mercury (mmHg) or numerically equivalent Torr.

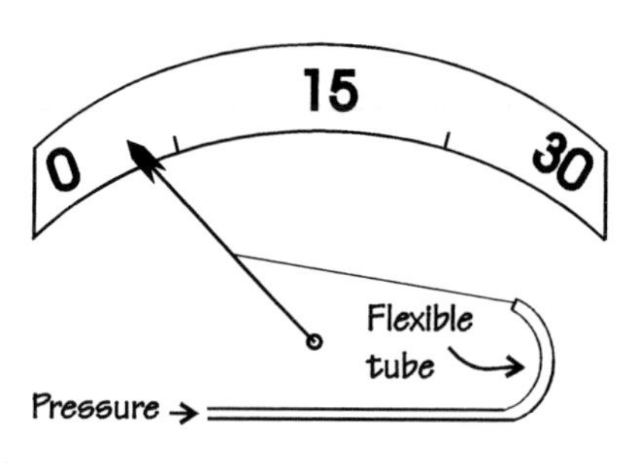

Figure 11-9 Rough vacuum gauge

High Vacuum

The gauge used to indicate high vacuum, in the micron or milli-Torr range, is the pirani gauge. This gauge compares the thermal loss of a heated wire in a partial vacuum to that of a gas transport that is pressure dependent. For nitrogen, the major constituent of air, the thermal energy transfer is directly related to pressure between one micron and about atmospheric pressure, seven hundred-sixty millimeters mercury. For neon gas, this linear function exists between one micron and one hundred millimeters mercury.

These gauges are particularly sensitive to flashback, a high voltage discharge through the manifold, and must be protected. Sudden exposure to atmospheric pressure and contamination from pump oil also must be avoided.

Butyl Oil Gauge

In the past, mercury filled gauges were used to measure gas fill pressure. However, butyl oil is now used because of its low vapor pressure, low chemical reactivity and density.

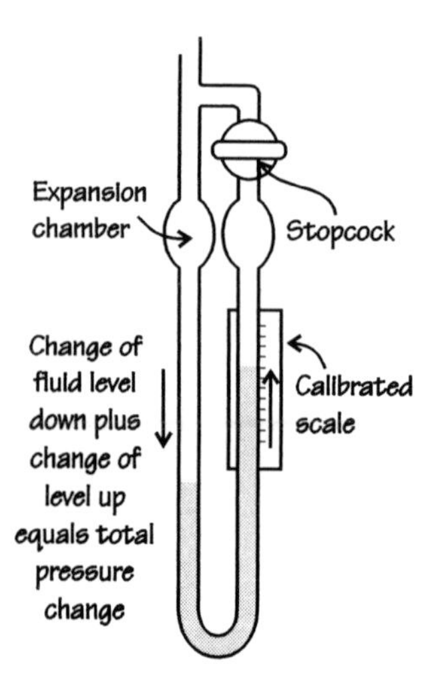

Figure 11-10 Butyl oil gauge

Butyl oil gauges are made in U-shape. Thus, the measure of pressure change is equal to the difference in height of the two fluid columns.

Butyl oil also is nearly fourteen times less dense than mercury. Thus, a given pressure will support a column of oil fourteen times higher: seven times on each side of the two fluid columns. This offers a proportional increase in accuracy over using mercury to measure gas fill pressure. When filled to ten millimeters pressure, a mercury column rises only five millimeters yet a butyl column rises thirty-five millimeters. A scale mounted on one side the gauge is calibrated with seven millimeters between each scale.

Measuring Bombarding Temperature

To gauge the tube temperature during bombarding, some technicians use a thin strip of dry newspaper as an indicator. They bombard until the paper chars indicating sufficient temperature. And this technique has served many well for sometime. However, using a temperature gauge guarantees proper tube temperature.

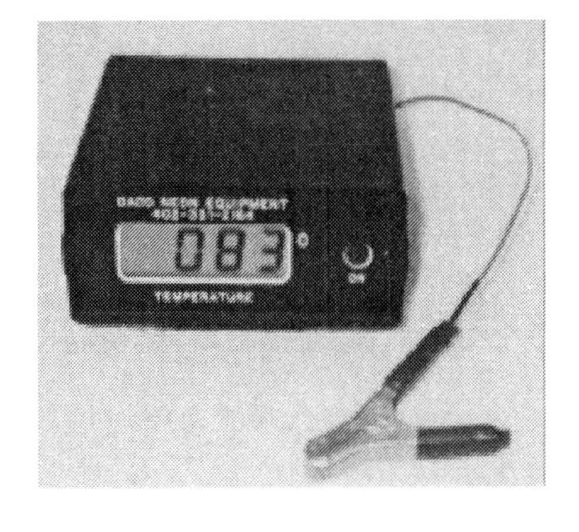

Figure 11-11
Digital tube temperature gauge
(Daco Neon Equipment)

Bimetal, Thermistor, Thermocouple Gauges and Crayons

Bimetal, thermistor and thermocouple gauges are examples of temperature gauges. Each converts heat into another form of energy, usually mechanical.

The bimetal gauge is inexpensive and works like the furnace thermostat found in most homes. It uses a strip of metal that expands with heat. The stretching metal strip twists around a needle at a predictable rate making an accurate measurement of thermal energy.

Thermistors respond rapidly to temperature changes and can be made very small. They make use of increasing electrical resistance with temperature in metals. The increase in resistance is nearly linear so long as the temperature change is not too great.

A thermocouple gauge is based upon the thermoelectric effect. Rather than measuring resistivity in metals, as with the thermistor, two dissimilar metals are joined at the ends. When the ends are at different temperatures, a relative voltage is produced. This voltage is applied across a needle that sweeps over a calibrated scale displaying the temperature change.

A thermal crayon is yet another method used to measure tube temperature. The colored crayon is made up of chemicals that change color when heated to certain temperature. The usual crayon used for neon tube processing change from green to brown then to black.

A tube temperature around four hundred twenty-five degrees Fahrenheit is required to vaporize common impurities found in a neon tube: nitrogen, oxygen, hydrogen, water, carbon monoxide and carbon dioxide. Yet, electrodes must be heated between sixteen hundred and eighteen hundred degrees Fahrenheit to process completely the emitter coating. No direct measurement of this temperature is made; rather the entire electrode shell is heated to glowing for several seconds.

Bombarding Instructions

Because equipment and manufacturing materials vary from shop to shop, bombarding methods usually vary a little too. The following bombarding instructions are intended for general use with minimal bombarding equipment. Always follow the equipment and electrode manufacturer's instructions for best results.

1.) Attach the unit by the tubulation to the manifold system.
2.) Place sheets of mica between glass bends spaced less than one tube diameter apart. This helps keep electricity from blowing through the glass tube.
3.) Attach bombarding leads to the electrodes and position the temperature indicator near the unit center.
4.) Turn on the vacuum pump (already warmed up).
5.) Close the vent or outside air stopcock.
6.) Set the choke according to electrode manufacturer specification.
7.) Open the vacuum or main stopcock.
8.) Immediately turn on the bombarding transformer and "bump" the dead man switch. Or, evacuate to specifications then activate the bombarder.
9.) If the tube lights, stay on the bombarding switch, close the vacuum stopcock and go on to number ten. If the tube does <u>not</u> light:

a.) Continue "bumping" every three or four seconds.

b.) If after a few more attempts the tube still does not light, simultaneously close the vacuum and butyl gauge stopcocks. <u>BE READY</u> to open quickly the gauge if sudden change occurs. This procedure shows large leaks and is called the "obvious leak test."

c.) If sudden change occurred in the gauge reading (and you

responded by opening the gauge to the manifold), open the vacuum stopcock. Use the spark coil to locate any leaks.

d.) If any leaks are found, bring the manifold to atmospheric pressure before separating the unit from the manifold (close the vacuum stopcock and open the vent). Repair any leaks and go back to step one. After repairing a large leak, higher vacuum develops and smaller leaks are detectable.

10.) Continue bombarding with the vacuum stopcock closed. Keep bombarding current between four and six times the electrode milliamperes rating or according to manufacturer specification. Heat the tube about one hundred twenty-five degrees Fahrenheit, stop bombarding and evacuate the tube for one minute to remove excess moisture. Close the vacuum and backfill gauge and fill the unit with two to three millimeters, or equivalently two or three Torr, of dry room air. Open the backfill gauge and continue bombarding.

Watch the ammeter for sudden movements. This would indicate a potential blow through about to occur. If this happens, get off the power and make a quick pass with the vacuum stopcock, open then close. Do not create too much vacuum. Too high a vacuum now could damage the electrodes by forcing early emitter coating processing.

11.) Once the tube reaches four hundred twenty-five degrees Fahrenheit, it is time to process the electrodes. Briefly increase the current ten to fifteen times the electrode rating and bombard until the full shell glows "cherry red" for several seconds. Or, follow electrode manufacturer instructions. Immediately switch off the bombarding current and open the vacuum to remove the gaseous impurities.

12.) Slightly warm tubulation tubing where the sign will be tipped off, one inch from the manifold side of a mercury trap or one-quarter inch from the pinch seal of a tubulated electrode. This liberates impurities outside the unit not submitted to bombardment.

13.) Once the tube has cooled to about one hundred degrees Fahrenheit, conduct a "backyard" vacuum test. Turn off the bombarder primary circuit and remove the high voltage lead *furthest* from the manifold. Apply the spark coil to the electrode wires. A healthy unit will light very faint blue or not at all. If it lights purple, a leak is present.

14.) Reconnect the high voltage wire, turn on the bombarding primary power and close the vacuum stopcock and the backfill gauge stopcock.

15.) Determine gas pressure from the appropriate chart considering tube diameter, type of gas and transformer.

16.) Gas the tube accordingly. If you overfill, reduce pressure in the tube by carefully opening the vacuum stopcock.
17.) With current set to minimum, depress the bombarding switch a couple seconds. Check for correct color within the tube, red/orange for neon gas and faint lavender for argon.

If the color is incorrect, open the backfill gauge and apply low bombarding current. Do this for sixty to ninety seconds. Open the vacuum stopcock and draw out remaining impurities for one minute or so. This technique uses the illuminating gas as a flushing agent. Commercial flushing gas is also available. Try gassing the unit again once the tube is pumped out.
18.) If the unit color is good, tip off the unit from the manifold.
19.) Use a transformer rated the same current as the electrodes and higher voltage to burn-in or stabilize the unit. Do this for two to eight hours when possible.
20.) There are two commonly used methods for neutralizing the manifold. One method is simply opening the backfill gauge. This leaves the manifold under vacuum. The second method requires opening both the backfill gauge and outside air stopcock. This technique fills the manifold with outside air to atmospheric pressure.

One drawback to this method is possible flask contamination. An inert gas flask that has filled several units is under vacuum. With the manifold at atmospheric pressure, the flask could draw outside air through a leaky stopcock and contaminate the pure gas. For this reason, the first method is often preferred.

Tip on Handling Mercury Spills

The average modern human body contains higher levels of mercury than our ancestors did. So, it is important to handle mercury safely to limit exposure. If a mercury spill occurs:
1) Ventilate the area.
2) Do NOT vacuum the spill.
3) Wear latex gloves.
4) Use a piece of heavy paper or cardboard to collect the beads.
5) Use masking, duct or other tape to gather smaller beads.
6) Collect the spill in an envelope then store in a sealable plastic bag.
7) Dispose through reclamation by using a licensed hazardous waste hauler or transport it to a local hazardous waste collection facility.

CHAPTER

12

Tube Painting, Mounting and Wiring

Once neon letters are made, welded together into a sign and lit, the tubing needs painting and support before put in use. Several paint and support methods exist and local codes sometimes dictate strict sign mounting and wiring procedures. Offered here are general techniques commonly used throughout the trade.

Blocking-out a Tube

Blocking-out a tube is painting out lengths of tubing meant not to be seen—such as areas between block letters, between words, etcetera. Special paint made for the neon industry is used to block light without conducting electricity. It is called "blockout paint" and is made either oil or water based and typically in the colors black, gray and white.

The paint is applied with a small brush or by dipping the finished unit into containers filled with the paint. Brushing on blockout is most commonly done on custom neon work. The unit is held so excess paint runs to the back rather than across the tube front. Stray paint is let dry because wet paint smears then scraped off with a razor or other blade.

Dipping tubes in blockout speeds the process and produces a clean look. Most mass produced signs, like beer signs, are painted in containers filled with blockout called "dip tanks." The finished tube is held face up then dipped gently into the paint so that the entire backside of the sign face and all sections of a tube bent off the table onto a block are coated completely.

Shops wanting to conserve blockout hang or rest the dipped units over a heavy plastic drop cloth, usually four or six mil thickness. Once dripping blockout paint dries on the plastic, it is lifted from it in sheets.

The sheets of paint are dropped back into the dip tanks where they dissolve back into the solution. Sometimes blockout thinner is added and stirred to help dissolve the paint.

Glass Frame Mounting

Glass frames are designed and manufactured by the neon craftsman. Also called skeleton framing, the structure is made of small clear glass tubing, usually eight to twelve millimeters in diameter. The framework is custom bent to match a sign and provides bracing to hang it.

To make a simple glass frame, anchor the finished sign tubing on the original pattern. Draw a glass frame pattern around the sign using a straight tube. Try to contact several points on each unit with this tube. Bend the glass frame to the pattern periodically checking fit with the neon units. Be sure the glass frame tubing has cooled before doing this.

Figure 12-1 Glass framing

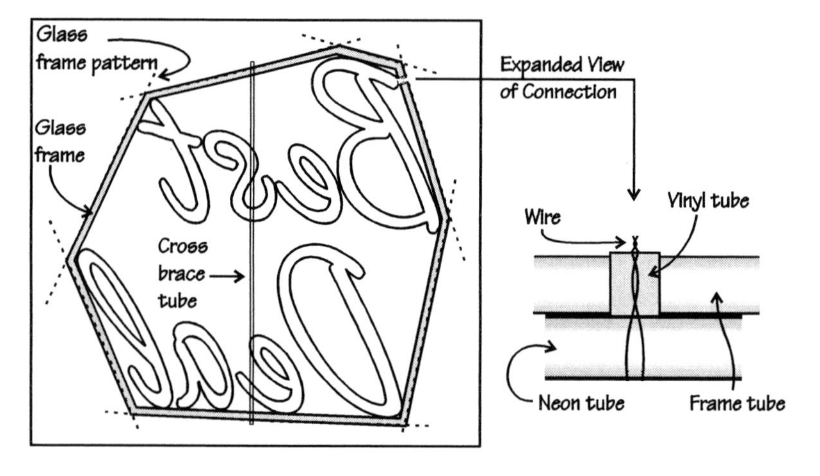

Before welding the frame into a single continuous tube, carefully measure the final piece and pre-cut to fit. Tubulate this tube then weld into place. Use the tubulation to work the final weld via the blowhose. Otherwise, do not tubulate and use the natural spring of the frame to jiggle weld the tubes together. Cross brace if needed with small clear glass tubing, five to eight millimeters in diameter.

Tie the frame to the sign at points of contact using clear vinyl tubing or masking tape as cushion. Apply the cushioning to the frame tube.

Use copper tie wire or nylon ties to fasten the frame to the sign. Then hang the sign by the frame with picture wire or chain. In almost all cases, mount the transformer to the wall above or below the sign but never to the glass frame.

Acrylic Back - Window Sign Mount

It is common to see neon window signs mounted to an acrylic backing. The acrylic provides a base for tube supports, transformer and adds background color. Tube supports or standoffs, as they are also called, elevate the tube above the acrylic. This leaves room for Doubleback bends and provides an insulating air gap between the tube and backing.

Figure 12-2 Common tube supports and proper positioning

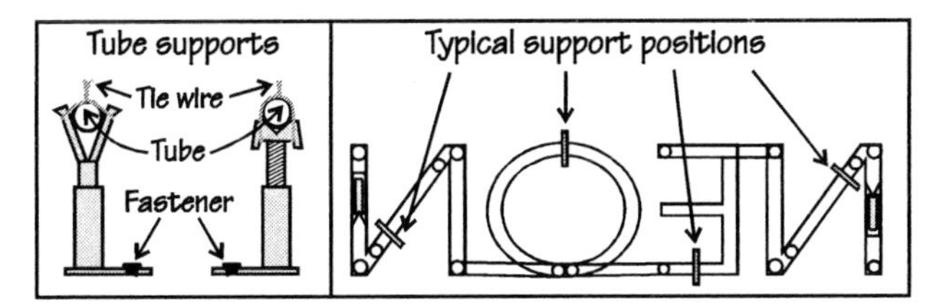

Tube supports are made of glass, nylon or plastic and most are height adjustable. Spring loaded standoffs act as shock absorbers providing extra protection against breakage during shipping.

Use too few supports and the tube is vulnerable to breakage. Use too many supports and sign appearance diminishes. Also, improperly positioned standoffs offer little or unbalanced support. It is best to position a support close to each electrode, within a few inches, without interfering with wiring and insulating. This effectively supports the end of each unit. Then stagger other supports high then low on a unit, top then bottom. This controls possible rocking motion during shipping or handling.

Tube support positions are marked on the acrylic backing and holes drilled before tube mounting. They are attached to the acrylic with screws or aluminum rivets except when acrylic supports are used. Acrylic supports are snapped onto the tubing, positioned on the acrylic backing then glued. The glue used is thin and dries quickly.

Bumpers often are added to the front or back corners of the acrylic. They protect the glass tubing from bumping into a window or keep the transformer and wiring from resting against a wall.

Exterior Signs - Tubes Penetrating a Structure

All exterior, outdoor tubes, and tubes penetrating interior walls in a public place are to be installed by licensed professionals according to electrical product safety testing agency standards. Common testing agencies include E.T.L. (Electrical Testing Laboratories), U.L. (Underwriter's Laboratories, Inc.) and C.S.A. (Canadian Standards Association). Approved products and signs are labeled with a sticker or tag as, "Listed." It is illegal to install these tubes otherwise. In addition, most places require a "Use Permit" be applied for and accepted before installation of any outdoor even some indoor signs.

Wiring a Sign

Neon tubes are wired together in electrical series; the components connected in a circle. They are wired successively by twisting electrode wires together or connecting with approved high voltage wire. Transformer voltage, gas fill and tube diameter all determine the number of units that can be connected on a circuit.

Figure 12-3 Common neon tube electrical connections

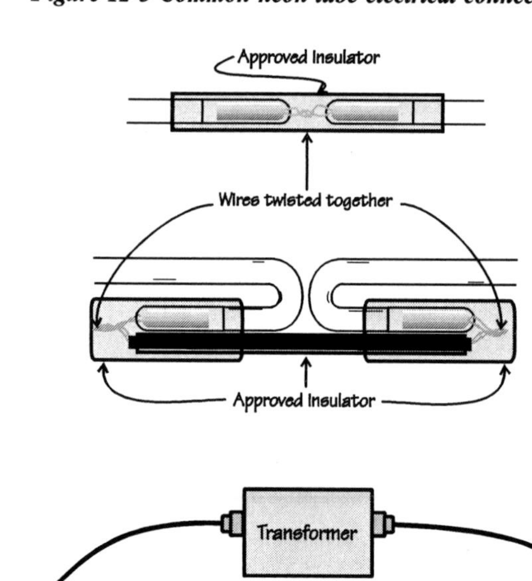

Transformer Types

Neon transformers are electrical, step-up type transformers. They operate at high voltage yet low current and are manufactured to suit a variety of installation conditions. The outdoor transformer is heavy and rugged. It is designed to withstand weather better than indoor or solid state transformers. It is not designed to be exposed directly to the elements however. So, outdoor transformers usually are mounted inside an electrically grounded metal box to safeguard the transformer, electrical wiring and public.

An indoor transformer usually is attached to the backside of an acrylic mounted sign or to the sill above it-which is why it is often called a "window" transformer. A drilled flange on the transformer base makes it easy to install with screws or bolts. A large window transformer uses a separate hanging bracket that is bolted to the sill above the sign then the transformer hung from it.

Figure 12-4 Two outdoor, compact window, core-n-coil, and solid state transformers (left to right)
(Transco)

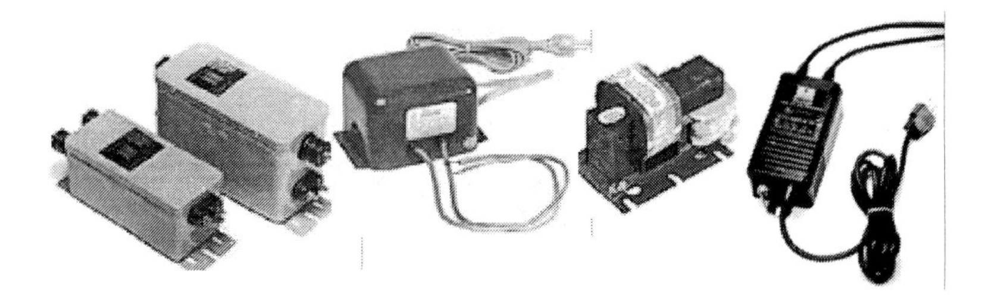

A core-n-coil is the exposed internal workings of a standard transformer: the metal core and the wired coil. These transformers are mounted in a grounded or double insulated housing to safeguard the public from harm. The core-n-coil appeal is its low cost and small size.

A solid state or electronic transformer is usually smaller than other types. It uses high frequency electricity to operate a tube more efficiently at somewhat lower voltage. Its electronic circuitry most often is housed in a plastic, lightweight body making it ideal for use in window signs or signs to be shipped. Several type mini-electronic transformers are made for use in neon artwork. Extra small and lightweight in design, these power sources are easily hidden behind or within an art piece.

Flawed electronic transformers can cause mercury migration. The unit dims slowly from one end until all the mercury in the tube collects on one electrode causing the unit to lose all brightness. A permanent remedy is to replace the transformer with one minus the flaw.

Heavy-Wall Insulators

Sometimes, it is the glass worker's responsibility to make custom electrode insulators. These insulators are made of large diameter, heavy-wall tubing manufactured especially for this use. Typically, these insulators are installed through walls or into sheet metal cans to house and protect electrodes and wire connections.

Make a heavy-wall electrode insulator by forming a flange on one end of the heavy-wall tube. There are many ways to do this, but a simple to make jig works best. To make the jig, mount four non-swiveling caster wheels to a base spacing them so the tube spins between the wheels.

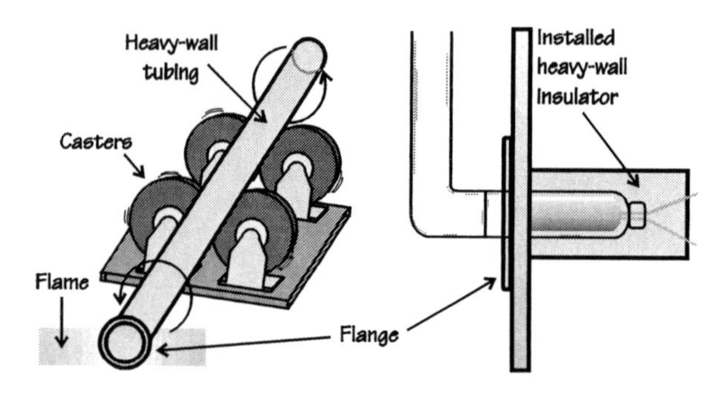

Figure 12-5 Making and using a heavy-wall insulator

Align the burner with the jig so the tube end enters the middle of the flame. Slowly move the tube into the flame while rotating it to assure even heat. As the end melts, spin the tube faster. The rotational forces cause the tube end to flare forming the flange. When the flare lip is about three-eighths of an inch deep, slowly back the tube away from the flame, still rotating the tube. This helps cool the glass slowly lessening chance of strain. Once cool, cut the tube a predetermined length from the flare, usually four to eight inches sometimes longer depending upon the installation. Attach the insulator by inserting through a hole drilled in the mount and secure with a bead of silicone or other retainer.

Transporting Neon

Getting completed neon tubing to its destination is a task best done carefully. So, most large units are tied to a rack made of wooden slats or chicken wire. The tubes are attached with copper tie wire or nylon zip ties. Some even tie the tubes to rubber anti-fatigue mats when extra cushion is needed as when the tubes are stacked several units deep. Then the tubes are tied to one another too. Once the tubes are securely fastened to the rack, they are hauled to the site by truck or on a trailer.

Build a simple hauling rack by screwing or nailing wood slats across a one-by-two or two-by-four frame as in Figure 12-6. Space the slats two to four inches apart. The rack dimension should fit the typical glass unit design and the truck or trailer. Keep the rack size manageable even if you are using a large truck or trailer. A typical rack measures three feet by six feet or four feet by eight feet.

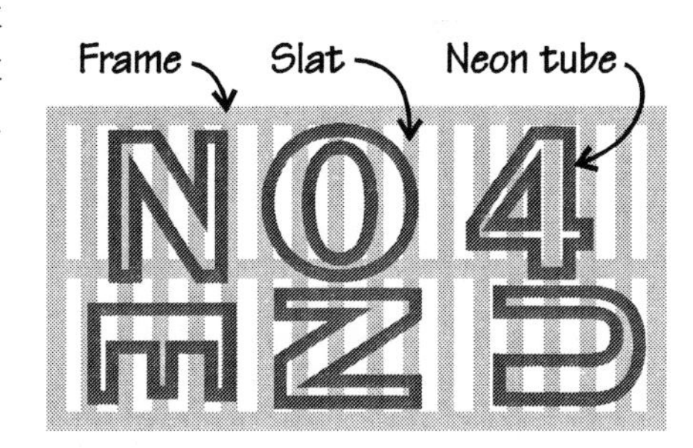

Figure 12-6 Typical rack used to transport neon tubes

Tips and Hints

1. Make the dip tank size fit the typical unit your shop manufactures. Too small a tank means a large unit must be blocked out by brush.
2. When using a dip tank, thin the blockout with liquid thinner according to manufacture guidelines. This allows better tube coverage, less drying time and is more economical.
3. To clean the exterior of old or dirty neon tubing, thoroughly spray with glass cleaner then immediately rinse with low-pressure water. This way even years of restaurant kitchen grease can be removed from the sign quickly with little risk of breakage.
4. Clean acrylic backing with approved acrylic cleaner or polish. Some cleaning liquids dull the material so choose the product carefully.
5. Use aluminum pop rivets with a washer when mounting tube supports to acrylic to lessen chance of cracking the plastic.
6. To form protective bumpers, use a heat strip to bend the acrylic backing. First, peel away a two inch wide strip of the protective paper covering the acrylic where the bend is to be formed. Peel the paper away from both sides of the acrylic. Use the heat strip to soften both

sides of the backing–flip the backing a couple times to heat evenly. Once softened, form a ninety-degree turn using a straight, flat board to sharpen the crease. Press the acrylic into a corner or over a table edge to aid forming the turn. Let cool several minutes then do the same to form the other bumper. Form the bumpers along the longest sign edge to add extra strength.

7. Become a licensed installer or hire one to install any exterior tubes or tubes penetrating a wall in a public place. Usually, it is illegal to install these tubes by anyone not licensed. Get your shop listed through a listing agency to limit liability.

Figure 12-7 and 12-8
Transporting serif channel letter tubes zip tied to a mat and Transporting channel letter units stacked and tied together

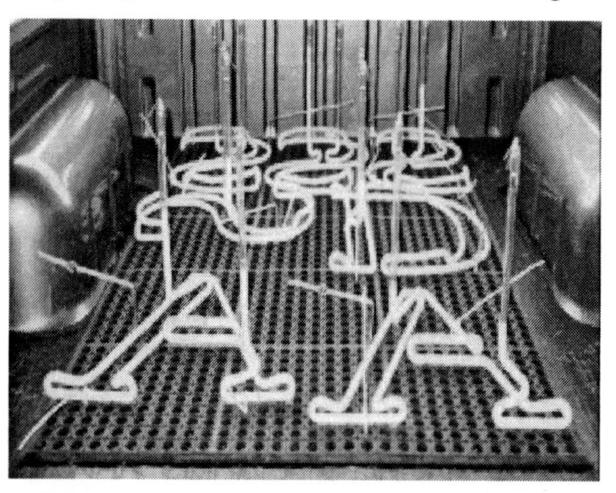

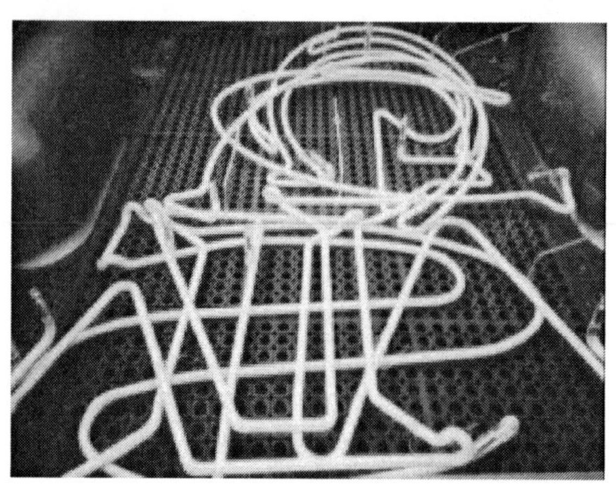

CHAPTER

13

Building a Simple Manifold

Manifold Function, Type and Design

The manifold function is to give the operator control of the environment in a glass tube during processing. Its principal components are the mainbody, stopcocks, flasks and traps.

Many types of manifold are available and are made of metal, borosilicate, soda or lead glass. Some may use greaseless stopcocks or even high-tech metal valves from the nuclear industry. Each manifold varies in cost and maintenance yet operate much the same. This chapter describes the construction of the least expensive yet highest maintenance manifold.

Manifold designs are limitless; however, manifold layout should fit the needs of the operator. If space is a priority, design a system to be mounted under a table or on a wall. If production is important, T- or Y-connectors allow pumping two to four units at a time.

The Mainbody

The mainbody of the manifold is the heart of the system. Through it, all hot impure gases travel to the vacuum pump. It is made of a large diameter tube, fifteen millimeter or bigger. A large diameter tube is necessary so pumping capacity is not restricted and pressure changes within the system are buffered.

This simple mainbody design uses less than four linear feet of fifteen millimeter tubing. It is made of one ribbon fire U-bend, two L-bends and five tubulations. Most of the tubulation are made of ten millimeter tubing and connect the mainbody to peripheral components. The right most and largest tubulation connects the mainbody and neon unit.

The bulb at the bottom right is an optional trap. This trap keeps mercury from entering the manifold and vacuum pump. The four inch gap between the left two tubulation allows room for welding then using gassing stopcocks. The seven inch space between the middle two tubes leaves room for a simple butyl oil gauge. The bent tubulation on the upper right is for outside air and blowhose access.

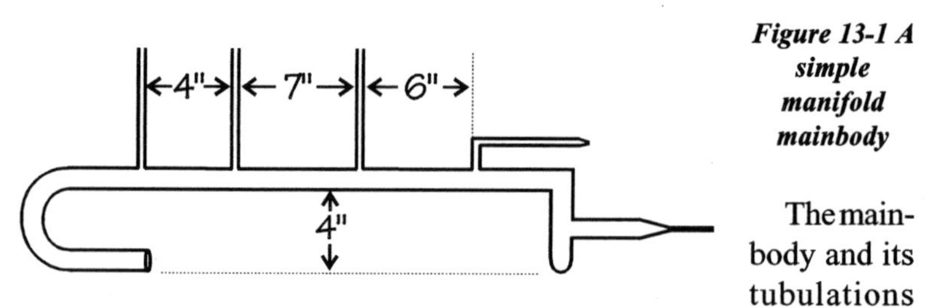

Figure 13-1 A simple manifold mainbody

The mainbody and its tubulations lay in one plane, flat. This makes it simple to attach the unit to a board or wall using standard tube supports. Once attached, the stopcocks, flasks and butyl gauge are welded into place. All stopcocks face toward the operator.

The T-Connector

A T- or Y-connector allows bombardment of two similar units at once, although some use one side to bombard mercury units and the other non-mercury units. This way if any mercury collects in the T it most likely will remain on the mercury side. Mercury combined with neon turns the gas color blue.

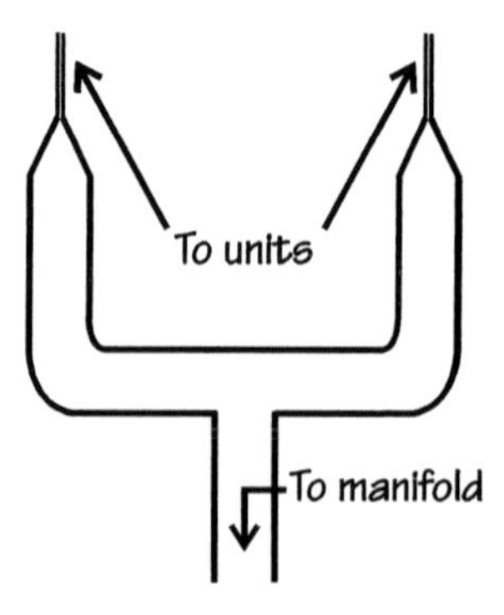

Figure 13-2 The T- or Y-connector

Changing a Gas Flask

Changing a rare gas flask is necessary when the flask is empty or when it is contaminated with outside air. Contamination occurs when one or more stopcocks leak or are opened necessarily. To change a flask, first neutralize the manifold, the main body and butyl gauge, to atmospheric pressure. Then open the gassing stopcocks between the manifold and the dead flask to neutralize it. Cut the flask from the manifold and remove the seal breaker, usually a metal bolt or ball bearing. Place the object in the new flask gently. Weld the new flask onto the manifold. While the weld is cooling, clean and grease the gassing stopcocks (see greasing a stopcock after this section). Now, evacuate the entire system with gassing stopcocks open to evacuate all the impurities.

Use the spark coil to check the freshly made weld for leaks. Use a low setting so not to puncture the seal. Then run the spark the full length of the tubing between the flask and stopcocks. This helps chase out moisture created while welding.

Once a high vacuum has developed and no leaks are detected, close the vacuum stopcock, the butyl gauge stopcock and the gassing stopcock closest to the new flask. Use magnets on both sides of the seal breaking object and lift it well above the seal. Remove the magnets so the object falls breaking the seal. More than one attempt is often necessary.

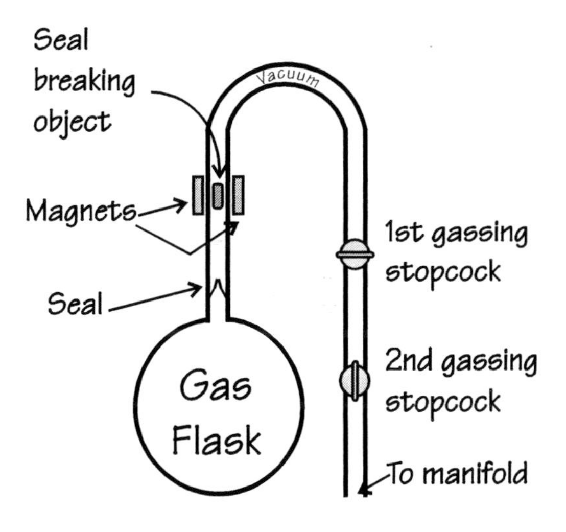

Figure 13-3 Readying a flask for use

Inert gas from the flask is present at the closed stopcock once the seal is broken. Slowly open this stopcock but really be ready to close the next gassing valve as soon as the butyl oil begins climbing. This makes the second gassing stopcock a control valve that is used when filling tubes. It makes the first stopcock a regulator used to slow the gas from the flask.

Ladle Filling

Another way to deliver inert gas to a unit is ladling. With a flask ready for use, close both flask stopcocks. Then rotate the first stopcock one-half turn, one hundred-eighty degrees. This charges with gas the length of tubing between the valves. Rotate the second stopcock to fill the unit. Repeat the procedure until the unit is filled to correct pressure. Large units may require several ladlings to fill.

Manifold Maintenance

Manifold maintenance consists of periodic greasing of stopcocks and cleaning the manifold tubing. Some use high-grade acetone to clean their systems, others use low vapor pressure, diluted acids. A low vapor pressure, grease-cutting formula is desired so little or no residue outgases into the system contaminating it.

Greasing a Stopcock

When greasing a stopcock, a suitable high vacuum grease must be used. The wrong grease will outgas under vacuum, possibly contaminating the system. Only a thin film of grease is required, too much grease and the bore hole becomes plugged. Run a bead of grease halfway between the bore hole and the top and bottom of the stopcock. Place little grease, if any, around the bore hole.

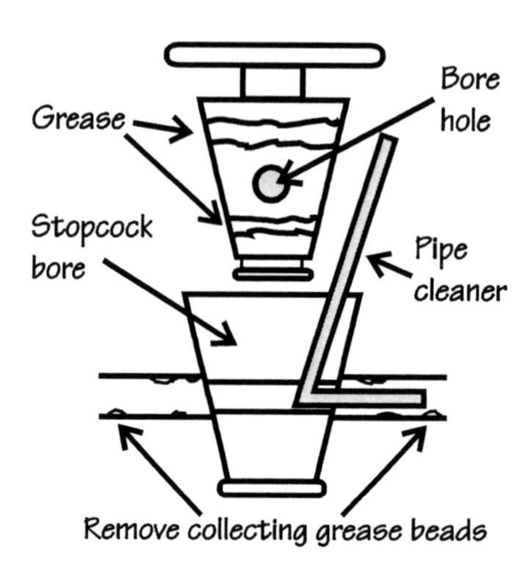

Figure 13-4 Cleaning and greasing a glass stopcock

Once the stopcock is properly greased, gently but firmly push the stopcock back into the bore. Make sure all visible air bubbles are driven out and no foreign material is within the seal. A couple turns of the stopcock helps form an airtight seal. Stopcocks are *not* interchangeable. Do not switch bores or they may leak. Grease them one at a time to be safe.

Stopcocks need greasing when they are difficult to turn or when they leak. A lightly greased, unused stopcock eventually will seize. With little care, grease type stopcocks last many years.

Tips and Hints - Manifold Flashback

Manifold flashback is a potentially dangerous phenomenon where during bombarding high voltage electricity travels through the manifold to the vacuum pump. Flashbacks usually occur when the manifold is under extreme vacuum and the main stopcock is open. Flashbacks seldom occur with the vacuum stopcock closed and they do not occur on all systems. Using the closed stopcock bombarding technique with a Jacob's Ladder almost ensures the operator safety during tube processing. Isolating the vacuum pump from electrical ground also discourages flashback.

Figure 13-5 Complete glass manifold system

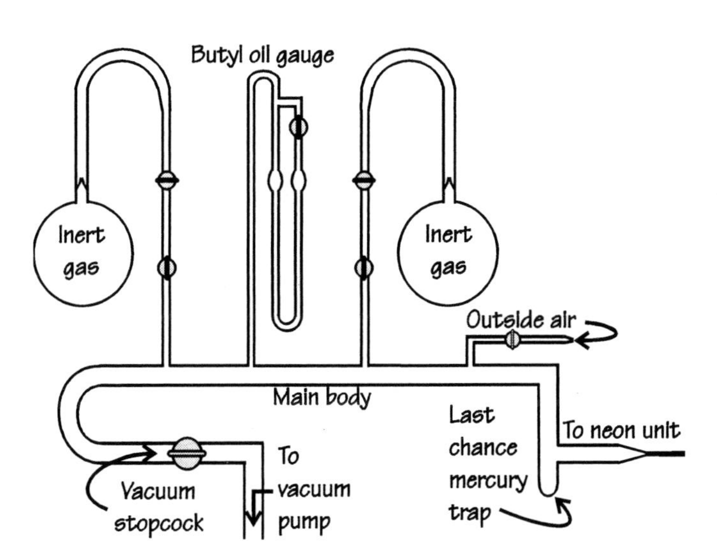

CHAPTER

14

Questions and Answers

Whenever a neon sign is sold, many questions beg answering: What size letters are needed? What diameter tube works best? How much tubing will be in the sign? What fee should be charged? What size transformer will run the sign? These questions and more are answered here using both text and tables.

Is The Sign Legible?

Table 14-1 is the Table of Legibility. The table considers basic colors and letter height since both are factors of legibility. The chart serves as a guide and not a strict determinate of typestyle, color and dimension.

Table Of Legibility			
Distances are approximate due to variables			
Letter Height (inches)	Red-Clear Neon (feet)	Blue Mercury (feet)	Green Mercury (feet)
2	65	50	42
4	150	115	98
6	200	150	130
8	350	260	227
10	450	340	290
12	525	395	340
18	750	560	490
24	1000	800	650
30	1250	940	815
(feet)			
3	1500	1125	975
4	2000	1500	1300
5	2500	1875	1625
6	3000	2250	1950
8	3750	3000	2600
10	4000	3750	3250

Table 14-1
Table of legibility

A business located on a sidewalk does not need twelve inch high, red letters. Most viewers are five feet away, not five hundred twenty-five feet away as the chart suggests. In fact, many would find at this distance a twelve inch letter sign obtrusive. An effective sign is readable and pleasing to the eye, both a messenger and a compliment in its function.

What Tube Diameter Should Be Used?

Once the size and style of letter is determined, a tube diameter is chosen to form the letter. Table 14-2 suggests tube diameters for both single and double stroke letters. Use too small a diameter tube on a large letter and the size and number of transformers required to light it increase.

Suggested Tube Diameter To Letter Height			
Single Stroke		Double Stroke	
Letter Height (inches)	*Tube Diameter (mm)*	*Letter Height (inches)*	*Tube Diameter (mm)*
3 to 5	9 or 10	5 to 7	9 or 10
6 to 8	12	8 to 10	10 or 12
9 to 12	12 to 15	11 to 15	12 or 13
13 up	15 up	16 up	13 up

Table 14-2
Suggested tube diameter

This is because small diameter tubes have high electrical resistance. On the other hand, use too large a diameter tube on a small letter and detail is lost and bending more difficult. Also, light density changes noticeably between tube diameters. Small diameter tubes light brighter than large diameter tubes due to increased current density.

How Much Tubing Is Needed?

Table 14-3 helps determine the number of linear feet of tubing in a sign.

Approximate Number of Linear Feet of Tubing Per Letter			
Letter Height (in inches)	Single Tube		Double Tube
	Block	Script	All
3	0.88	1.25	1.38
4	1.17	1.67	1.83
5	1.46	2.08	2.29
6	1.75	2.5	2.75
7	2.04	2.92	3.21
8	2.33	3.33	3.67
9	2.63	3.75	4.13
10	2.92	4.16	4.58
11	3.21	4.58	5.04
12	3.5	5	5.5

Table 14-3
Linear feet of tubing per letter

Simply locate the letter height, slide horizontally right to the proper column, then multiply the number of letters in the sign by the factor. Because there are many styles of letters and letter width, the table is only an approximation. Use a map wheel on the finished pattern to determine linear footage accurately.

A simple formula is often used to determine linear tube length: (Number of letters) times (letter height in inches) times (3.5 for block letters) or (5.0 for script letters) or (5.5 for double stroke letters) divided by (12) equals approximate linear tube footage.

How Much Glass Should I Buy?

Table 14-4 offers packaging information for clear glass tubing. Consider a sign consisting of twenty-eight linear feet of ten millimeter clear tubing. The sign requires about two pounds of ten millimeter glass—twenty-eight linear feet divided by fourteen linear feet per pound equals two pounds. Of course, no margin for error is considered so ordering extra glass is prudent.

Table 14-4 Tube packaging information

Tube Per Pound Information (Four Foot Clear Tubes)							
Diameter in millimeters	8	9	10	11	12	13	15
Sticks per pound	4.5	4	3.5	3	2.75	2.25	1.8
Linear feet per pound	18	16	14	12	10.5	9	7.25

What Do I Charge?

Pricing methods vary widely across the country and often in the same city. Wholesale prices reflect a discount given to sign companies that sell neon but do not manufacture it. Retail prices reflect end market value or customer pricing. Company and local economics play factor in any final price. Nevertheless, the method used to determine the sign price should be profitable and consistent.

The simplest method is the price-per-letter system. A price is set for a given letter height and style: (x) dollars for under six inch block letters, (y) dollars for six inch to ten inch block letters, (z) dollars for four inch and smaller script letters, etcetera. The number of letters multiplied by the price-per-letter charge is added to transformer, mounting, installation and other cost.

Another way to price is by the linear foot of tubing; most wholesale shops use this method. A different dollar value is set for block, script and other styles. A higher value is set for coated tubes, double coated tubes and large letters. This fee is multiplied by the approximate number of linear feet of tubing in the sign. Transformer, mounting and any other costs are added to determine final price.

Wholesale Prices Per Linear Foot 10mm through 15mm Tubing			
Tube Colors	Block Letters	Script or Double	Straight Borders
Clear	$4.95	$5.50	$3.95
White, Green, Blue, Turquoise	$5.25	$5.75	$4.25
Neo-blue, Gold, Purple, Deep green, Yellow, Pink	$5.95	$6.50	$4.75
1. Add 1 foot for each pair of electrodes 2. Add $1 per serif 3. Minimum charge is $35.00 4. Shop rate is $50.00 per hour			

Table 14-5 Wholesale price example

Which Transformer Do I Use?

Table 14-6 is the Luminous Tube Transformer Chart. It helps determine the correct transformer for a sign based on tube diameter, type of inert gas and tube length. Gas pressures are located conveniently above the tube diameters. Transformer size is on the left.

How To Use The Transformer Chart - Simple Example

To determine proper transformer size for a single tube diameter-single gas unit, first locate the correct tube diameter in the Tube Size In Millimeters row.

Next, move down the column until a chart number matches the number of linear feet of tubing in the sign. If a number does not match, choose one larger. It is better to overpower than to underpower a unit.

Finally, move horizontally left across the chart to the Secondary Voltage column under the Standard Transformer Rating heading. This number represents the size of transformer recommended for the sign.

To be sure this is the correct transformer size, connect a milliammeter in electrical series with the unit and transformer. A properly loaded transformer reads about eighty percent of the transformer current rating. Ideally, a twenty milliamperes transformer reads sixteen milliamperes; a thirty milliamperes transformer reads twenty-four milliamperes; and a sixty milliamperes transformer runs at forty-eight milliamperes. A variance of about one-half of one percent is tolerable.

Multiunit, Single Gas Example

To determine the transformer size for a multiunit—single gas sign, begin with the smallest tube diameter and work toward the largest. Consider a sign made of three units all filled with argon and mercury. One unit is nine feet of ten millimeter tubing. The second unit consists of seven feet of twelve millimeter tubing and the final unit is sixteen feet of fifteen millimeter tubing.

First, look in the ten millimeter column under Mercury Filled and Tube Size In Millimeters. Find the number nine, the number of feet of tubing in the first unit. Next, slide horizontally right to the twelve millimeter column and come upon the number twelve. This is the number of feet of tubing, in terms of twelve millimeter tubing, the transformer "sees" equivalent. As far as the transformer is concerned, nine feet of ten millimeter tubing is equivalent to twelve feet of twelve millimeter tubing. This lets us combine the ten millimeter and twelve millimeter. Do this by adding the number of feet of twelve millimeter tubing in the sign to this number, seven feet (the number of feet of twelve millimeter tubing in the sign) plus twelve (the new number) equals nineteen. Move vertically up the twelve millimeter column to the number nineteen.

Now, to put this in terms of the next size tube diameter, slide horizontally right to the fifteen millimeter column. The new number is twenty-four. Add to this new number the actual number of feet of fifteen millimeter tubing from the sign and move vertically to the sum, twenty-four plus sixteen equals forty.

Therefore, nine feet of ten millimeter plus seven feet of twelve millimeter plus sixteen feet of fifteen millimeter, all mercury filled, is electrically equivalent to forty feet of fifteen millimeter mercury filled–so far as the transformer is concerned.

Before choosing the transformer, add the electrical resistance contributed by the electrodes. This is equivalent to one foot of tubing per pair of electrodes. In this example, there are three units or three pair of electrodes. So, adding three feet to the number forty under the fifteen millimeter column results in forty-three feet of electrical resistance seen by the transformer.

Sliding horizontally to the Secondary Voltage column, we see the chart recommends a nine thousand volt transformer. This transformer could be one of many kinds of transformer. However, only by checking with a milliammeter can we be certain that a nine thousand volt transformer will best operate this sign.

Multiunit, Gas and Tube Diameter Example

Determining transformer size for a sign made of many units, several tube diameters and filled with varying gases requires organization.

Table 14-6a Gas pressure and transformer chart for mercury tubes

Standard Transformer Rating	Mercury Filled Tubes						
	Recommended Gas Pressure In mm/Hg						
	13	12	11	10	9	8	7.5
Secondary Voltage	Tube Size In Millimeters						
	10	11	12	13	15	18	20
15000	44	48	54	60	72	80	90
12000	35	38	42	46	55	70	70
9000	25	28	31	33	40	55	55
7500	20	23	25	27	31	35	39
6000	16	18	19	21	24	28	32
5000	12	13	16	16	20	23	27
4000	9	10	12	13	16	19	22
3000	7	8	9	10	12	14	16
2000	5	6	7	8	9	Linear feet of tubing operated	

Making a chart that considers unit length, tube diameter and fill gas organizes this information. Consider the sign in Table 14-8. Note the total unit length with electrodes is listed in the final column.

Begin by locating the number seven under the ten millimeter, Mercury Filled column in Table 14-6. Slide horizontally to the next tube diameter found in the example, thirteen millimeter. There, we find the number, ten. Add the thirteen millimeter, mercury filled footage from the sign, six, and move up the thirteen millimeter column to the total, sixteen.

Again, slide horizontally to the next tube diameter column, ten millimeter neon filled. Here, we find the next number, ten.

Table 14-6b Gas pressure and transformer chart for neon gas tubes

Luminous Tube Transformer Chart — add one foot of tubing for each pair of electrodes

Neon Filled Tubes						
Recommended Gas Pressure In mm/Hg						
13	12	11	10	9	8	7.5
Tube Size In Millimeters						
10	11	12	13	15	18	20
36	40	45	50	60	72	78
29	32	35	39	45	55	61
21	24	26	29	33	40	48
17	19	21	22	26	28	34
13	15	16	18	20	23	28
10	11	12	15	17	19	23
8	9	10	11	13	16	19
6	7	8	9	10	11	12
4	5	5	6	7	Linear feet of tubing operated	

Figure 14-7 Milliammeter
(Daco Neon Equipment)

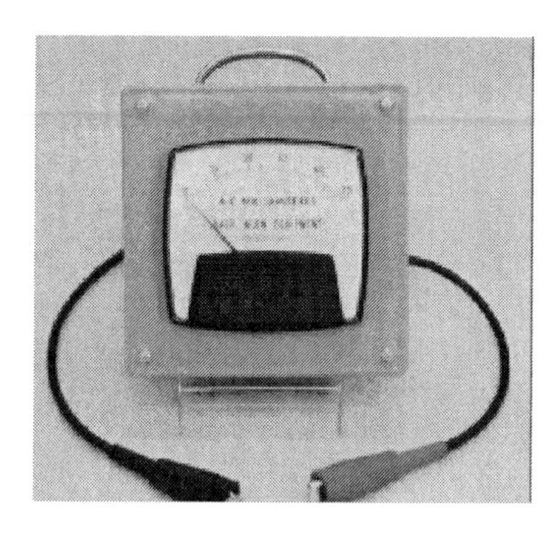

Add eight to this number, the total length of tubing in the sign, and move vertically up the ten millimeter column to the total, eighteen. Notice there is no number eighteen on the table? So, choose seventeen.

Now slide horizontally to the twelve millimeter column and pick up the number, twenty-one. Add the four feet from the sign and move vertically to the total, twenty-five. Again, compromise and choose the number twenty-six.

Table 14-8 Complex sign chart

Organizational Chart for Multi-unit, Multi Gas Fill and Tube Diameter Sign			
Unit Length in feet	Tube Diameter in millimeters	Fill Gas	Unit Length with electrodes
6	10	Mercury	7
5	13	Mercury	6
7	10	Neon	8
3	12	Neon	4
12	15	Neon	13
List units in order of increasing tube diameter and from mercury filled to neon filled			

Move horizontally to the fifteen millimeter column to the number, thirty-three. Add thirteen to thirty-three and move up the column to forty-six approximating the result with the number forty-five.

Sliding horizontally to the far left, we find a twelve thousand volt transformer should light the sign. Because this is only an approximation, it is important to use a milliammeter to be certain this is the correct size transformer for the project.

When using Table 14-6, notice the motion always follows a right-ascending staircase pattern. Any other motion means the table is being used incorrectly.

Solid state transformers operate at high electric frequency and do not require metering. Most are self-regulating meaning, if a transformer completely lights a tube, it is the correct size transformer. If it does not light it, a higher voltage transformer is needed.

How Much Power Does A Transformer Use?

Standard neon transformers use little electricity to operate a sign. A typical six inch OPEN sign operates on a three thousand volt transformer. This transformer uses only about forty-two watts of power, less than a single light bulb, yet produces significant light. Table 14-9 shows approximate wattage used and other electrical properties of standard sixty-cycle, 30mA transformers.

Standard Transformer - Normal Power Factor - Electrical Information

Secondary Voltage 30 m.a.	Approximate Wattage Used	Primary Amperage	Capacity Volt - Amps
15000	225	3.9	450
12000	180	3.13	360
9000	125	2.17	250
7500	115	1.96	230
6000	90	1.56	180
5000	75	1.3	150
4000	50	0.78	90
3000	42	0.65	75
2000	29	0.43	50

Table 14-9 Transformer information

Most conventional transformers rated over nine thousand volts are constructed like two separate transformers to balance the circuit. Solid state transformers are built and operate differently. They run at high frequency, much greater than sixty cycles per second. They light a tube more efficiently, consume less power and weigh much less than conventional transformers.

What About Inert Gases?

Table 14-10 offers characteristics of inert gases. By the Approximate Percent of Air by Volume column, it is easy to see why inert or noble gases are also called rare.

Table 14-10
Inert gases information

Inert Gas Characteristics				
Gas Name	Chemical Formula	Molecular Weight	Approximate % of Air by Volume	Specific Volume (cubic feet per pound)
Helium	HE	4.003	0.000054	96.7
Neon	NE	20.18	0.001	19.2
Argon	AR	39.95	0.93	9.7
Krypton	KR	83.8	0.000015	4.6
Xenon	XE	131.3	0.000003	2.9

So This Is Chemistry?

Table 14-11 is a portion of the Periodic Table of the Elements. The number below each element symbol is the atomic mass. With inert gases, the larger the atomic mass the bigger the atom size. The bigger the atom size the easier the gas is to light, it requires less voltage to light. Hence, a given transformer will light more linear feet of similar tubing, more krypton than argon, argon than neon, etcetera.

Table 14-11
Chemistry table

Periodic Table Of The Elements (Nonmetals)					
The Shaded Column At Right Indicates Rare, Noble Or Inert Gases					2 He 4.0026
5 B 10.811	6 C 12.011	7 N 14.0067	8 O 15.9994	9 F 18.9984	10 Ne 20.179
	14 Si 28.806	15 P 30.9738	16 S 32.064	17 Cl 35.453	18 Ar 39.948
		33 As 74.9216	34 Se 78.96	35 Br 79.904	36 Kr 83.80
			52 Te 127.6	53 I 126.904	54 Xe 131.30
				85 At (210)	86 Rn (222)

Am I A Good Glassblower?

No standards are established to help qualify glassblower ability. So, Table 14-12 offers quantitative production and quality standards. It considers the number of bends made per minute, variations from the pattern and the number of marginally acceptable bends.

Table 14-12
Ability qualification

Glassblower Ability Qualification Table				
Qualification	Minutes Per Bend (MPB)	Variations From The Pattern (VP)	20 Maneuver "Open" Sign	Marginally Acceptable Bends (MAB)
Novice	5 and up	20% up	100 plus minutes	20% to 25%
Entry Level	3 1/2 to 5	15% to 20%	70 to 100 minutes	10% to 20%
Journeyman	2 1/2 to 3 1/2	0% to 15%	50 to 70 minutes	5% to 10%
Journeyman Production	1 1/2 to 2 1/2	0% to 10%	30 to 50 minutes	0% to 5%

Minutes Per Bend

The Minutes Per Bend column suggests a value for each level of qualification. This value is determined by adding the number of maneuvers from a pattern including bends, welds and tubulations. By timing a neon project from beginning to finish then dividing the number of minutes to project completion by the number of maneuvers, the average number of minutes per bend is determined.

Variations from the Pattern

The Variations From The Pattern column helps classify a craftsman's bending accuracy. This requires an accurately drawn pattern to allow close determination of variation and to give the glass worker an accurate blueprint from which to work. Consider an acceptable variation one-half tube diameter from the pattern on a standard six-inch OPEN sign.

Marginally Acceptable Bends

The number of Marginally Acceptable Bends is subjective. A value based on a percentage of the number of bends is valid. The definition of a marginally acceptable bend is left to the judge.

As every glassblower knows, ability varies from day to day, sometimes from hour to hour. There are limits to the speed a craftsman can happily attain. A single test on a given day does not give an accurate view of ability. A good test includes many projects over several days.

How Do I Repair Broken Tubes?

First determine if the tube had mercury in it; ask what color the tube was when lit then look at the electrode shell. If the tube had a red or orange hue when lit, chances are good it was gassed with neon and contains no mercury. If the electrode shell is clean, free from mercury, it is a neon unit. Begin all repairs by tracing the entire tube. This way, if the tube is destroyed, it can be remade.

Repair clear tubes by cutting away the broken segment. Bend the segment, weld into place, change the electrodes and process the unit. Repair coated tubes by cutting away the broken segment and any length with phosphor coating blown out—sudden breaks let air rush in peeling the powder from inside the tube. Occasionally, it is best to remake the entire unit. Use dry, compressed air to blow remaining loose coating from the tube. Then remake the segments, weld into place, change the electrodes and process the unit.

If mercury is present, decide whether to take the risk of repair. Heating a mercury filled tube releases mercury vapors. Mercury vapors are extremely toxic affecting the nervous system over time. Some shops refuse to repair mercury tubes preferring to remake them instead. Others rinse the broken tube with distilled water into a container. After the water evaporates, the mercury is collected with a mercury spill kit and disposed of with the proper local environment protection agency. The tube is blown dry with low pressure, dry air and is repaired as previously described.

How Are Neon Transformers Typically Rated And Tested?

Neon transformers commonly are described by their open circuit output voltage expressed in thousands of volts and their secondary short circuit electrical current expressed in milliamperes. A volt is a force, an electric potential between two or more points and could be considered the "push" of electricity. When a neon tube is wired in series with the transformer and the transformer is switched on, the tube initially impedes this push with great force. However, upon lighting the tube's resistance drops quickly and a transformer that is properly "loaded" will show that the secondary voltage has dropped to about half its rated capability.

Many conventional transformers are designed with a midpoint ground where the transformer secondary assembly is physically split in two equal halves. For example, a 12,000-volt balanced midpoint grounded transformer houses two separate secondary coils. Each coil produces 6,000 volts from its respective terminal to electrical ground. From terminal to terminal, the voltage is additive and measures 12,000 volts. A balanced midpoint design houses the primary coil between the two secondary coils whereas an unbalanced midpoint design holds the primary coil separate from the two secondary coils. However, only the balanced design operates like two independent transformers as the unbalanced design is magnetically coupled; each coil affects the other. This bears upon installation in that only the balanced design can be "midpoint wired."

Most transformers rated 9,000 volts or more are midpoint grounded. It is possible that a damaged or flawed midpoint ground secondary coil could cause the transformer to malfunction. So, it is important to short circuit meter each secondary terminal to electrical ground using the proper equipment. A properly functioning coil will offer half the transformer voltage rating. It is very important to follow all test equipment instructions for your safety as well as that of the equipment.

Secondary electric current is stated on the transformer in secondary short circuit milliamperes. Now, a milliampere is 1/1000 of an amp and is a measure of the "flow" of charged particles, the flow of electricity. These charged particles move because a potential difference exists, a voltage, between two or more points. Short-circuited, the transformer current should measure the stated value, i.e. 30mA on a rated 30mA transformer. And when a transformer is properly loaded with tubing, the secondary current should drop to about 80% of the transformer short circuit rating for argon/mercury tubes and 85% for neon tubes. Flickering may occur if the current is much less than these values and transformer overheating may occur if it is much more.

Speaking of flickering, another test of transformer operation is the "flicker test." Here the primary voltage supply is dropped until the sign tubes begin to flicker. For a typical transformer rated at 120 volts, tube flicker should not occur before the primary voltage is decreased to around 90 volts or about 75% of normal. If the sign does flicker, consider stepping up to the next larger size transformer.

Transformers are also rated by their Power Factor. The term relates to a property where the transformer's measured power consumption does not accurately reflect the power used; the transformer in effect fools the electric meter into reading less current. So, some regions require that a High Power Factor transformer be used to more accurately depict electrical consumption. The higher a transformer's power factor, the closer a circuit can be described by its volt-amps.

Can I Install My Signs?

Some areas do not enforce any codes governing indoor sign installation. However, most areas require a sign be manufactured according to a set of rules using accepted materials and sign installation is strictly governed, especially outdoor installations. The process usually involves applying for a permit paid for by the sign manufacturer. A local governing body decides whether to permit the sign use. Upon issuance of the permit, the sign is installed then inspected by a sign inspector before operation.

All outdoor signs or tubes mounted into or on a wall in a public place require installation by a licensed sign installer working for a company that is "listed" with a listing agency, such as E.T.L. (Electrical Testing Laboratories), U.L. (Underwriter's Laboratories, Inc.) and C.S.A. (Canadian Standards Association). These agencies inspect sign shops for accepted materials use and assembly methods for a fee. Some regions do not require this of portable window signs. Always check rules regarding installation in your area before installing a sign.

Is A Neon Sign Advertising?

As defined by Webster's Dictionary, advertising is "the action of calling something to the attention of the public." A neon sign certainly does that. Knowing the value a sign contributes to business image and its potential for increasing sales is not the industry mindset today. Compare any other business advertising cost and a neon sign is extremely cost effective. In fact, compare advertising industry billing methods and a neon sign is implausibly inexpensive.

CHAPTER

15

Neon Art

Crackle Tubes

When lit, crackle tubes appear to contain bolts of lightning the color of the inert gas fill. They are used as special effects in many of today's science fiction television shows and movies. They are tubes or plates of glass filled with crushed glass, glass beads or other nonconducting material. The restrictions between the fill particles cause electrical current to flow down many pathways simultaneously. Because the pathways are restricted, the current density through them is high and therefore bright. After one path lights, it often is easier for the current to flow down another path lighting it. As such, the changing brightly-lit paths appear to strike like lightning, to crackle.

When making a simple crackle tube be certain no glass strains exist in the work. Do this by carefully manufacturing the tube; allow all maneuvers to cool properly before making the next move or anneal the finished tube in a special oven. Any strain in the work increases the chance of breakage during processing. Also, the fill adds cumbersome weight to the unit so handle carefully.

A crackle tube is made of large diameter, fifteen millimeter or bigger, clear glass. Greater tube volume offers room for more fill creating additional pathways for effect. It also helps reduce electrical resistance within the tube.

During normal bombarding, a crackle tube heats much faster than a regular tube. This is partly due to spatial restriction but also because additional impurities adhere to the fill. For this reason, baking the tube in an oven is preferred to conventional bombarding though both processes are used. Uncoated electrodes aid the process since proper coating conversion is not possible without use of an induction coil.

To reduce the number of impurities, clean the fill with dilute acid and distilled water before insertion. The particles must be thoroughly dry before use, however, for the cleaning liquid ultimately is also a contaminant.

Fill resting on electrodes causes problems during bombarding because electrodes exceed the melting point of glass, if glass fill is used. For this reason, an oven is often used. However, for those lacking an oven, the tube can be successfully processed with a few changes to normal bombarding.

Because the tube temperature increases very quickly during normal bombarding, heat the tube in increments. That is, activate the bombarder a few seconds then release it a couple seconds and let the tube rest. This allows the temperature gradient to balance within the tube minimizing hot spots that could cause strain in the tube. Repeat this procedure many times until the tube reaches proper temperature.

In addition, frequent vacuuming is necessary as more impurities are present and freed inside the tube. A vacuum gauge shows the rapid rise in pressure as the impurities vaporize. To remove them, rotate the vacuum stopcock during the seconds of rest. Try to maintain a pressure between two and four millimeters mercury.

Some final tips, connect the piece to the manifold with a well-greased section of high vacuum hose. Rotate the tube to jostle the fill particles during processing; this exposes more fill surface area. When handling the tube during processing, observe all safety precautions. The tube is extremely hot to touch and bombarding electricity is potentially lethal. Use uncoated electrodes or an induction coil since proper electrode conversion temperature usually cannot be reached.

Color Changing Tubes

There are a couple ways to cause neon tubes to change color. One method requires no extra equipment, comprising simply of a neon filled tube and mercury vapor. The other method uses combinations of gases and a special transformer that cycles electrical frequency and waveforms to stimulate these different gases to luminous levels. Each gas lights with its own distinct color when stimulated: helium lights pinkish, neon-orange/red, argon-violet and xenon-bluish white. Here, we discuss the first color changing method in detail.

Mercury vapor turns any lit inert gas blue in color. The reasons neon gas with mercury is not typically used commercially include:

1. Argon is more prevalent in the atmosphere than neon gas.
2. Argon requires less voltage per linear foot to light than neon gas.
3. Argon/mercury filled tubes only dim in cold weather applications whereas neon/mercury tubes unwontedly change color. The argon/ mercury combination dims because when chilled, the mercury vapor returns to liquid where it gives off no light. This is also the reason the neon/mercury tube changes color to neon red.

The trick to making a successful color changing tube is to balance the amount of mercury vapor to that of tube volume. No one has done the homework to make this process convenient and repeatable. However, here are some tips:

1. Place a very small amount of mercury in a trap a couple of inches away from the neon unit.
2. After burning-in, light the unit with the transformer it will operate on upon completion.
3. Now, carefully pass a handtorch or heat gun across the trap. A turquoise glow will signal the transfer of mercury vapor to the unit.
4. When a few inches of a small unit turns the color mercury-blue, quickly remove the mercury trap. Large units need several inches of tube to turn blue before tipping-off the trap.

If properly filled, the colors neon-red with mercury-blue move slowly but freely about clear glass tubing. And each time the unit is turned off allowed to cool then turned on again, the blue is found in different areas throughout the unit. Neon/mercury vapor in coated tubes offers similar results except the colors compliment the phosphor color: changing pink and orange in pink tubing, changing blue and rose in blue tubing, changing peach and turquoise in turquoise tubing and changing magenta and purple in some purple tubes, etcetera.

Patterns in Coated Tubes

Removing some phosphors from a coated tube allows the inert gas color to shine through the coating. A mercury filled—pink tube will glow both pink and blue, a mercury filled—green tube produces green and blue color combination and a neon filled— neo-blue tube exhibits mauve and neon-red. Many other color combinations are possible but it is the design created in the powder that interests most artists.

Removing the coating in a pattern creates a striking result, dashes and spirals are some designs used. Each requires practice to produce as the coating is well adhered inside the tube. Pipe cleaners and cotton swabs work well to pull the powder in short tubes. And a silicone dabbed- or felt pad tabbed-wood dowel works nicely on long lengths. Neatly weld short patterned tubes together to create longer patterns.

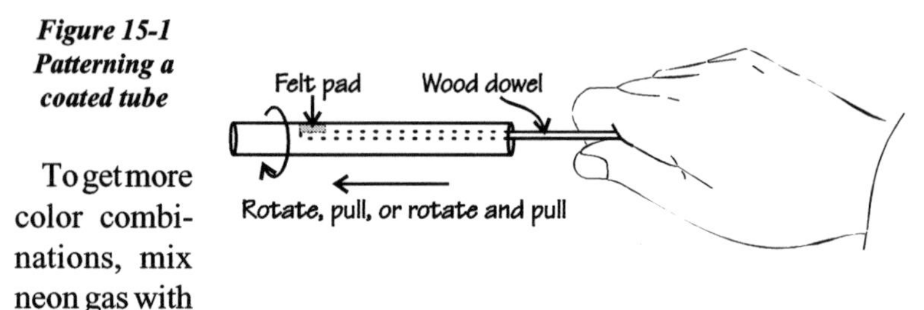

Figure 15-1 Patterning a coated tube

To get more color combinations, mix neon gas with mercury vapor in a pattern coated tube. A successful tube results in several alternating colors. Want even more? Weld together several pattern coated tubes and fill with neon gas and mercury vapor.

Snaking and Light Lasing

Making a tube snake on purpose is a tricky matter. The phenomenon is caused when at least two impurities are present in the tube; one is heavier than the inert gas fill and one is lighter. The path of electrons through the tube is one that assumes a path of least resistance. The light follows a narrow path of ever-displaced inert gas molecules causing the light to snake through the tube.

Sometimes snaking develops when insufficient tube processing has occurred, the tube is not heated sufficiently or it is not pumped thoroughly. Some artisans intentionally introduce tiny amounts of dry air into the tube producing the effect. However, snaking can reduce the life of a tube.

Other artisans cause a laser effect in a tube. They produce a bright, narrow path of light the color of the inert gas fill. The gas pressure in the tube is doubled, tripled or more causing inert gas atoms to pack ever tighter in the tube. Choosing the path of least resistance, electricity takes a narrow, shortcut-taking path through the tube. The beam is so narrow and bright it appears like a bending laser beam.

The effect has some drawbacks though, heat and shortened tube life. The densely packed electron beam increases current density raising tube temperature. The temperature can reach a point where the tube is too hot to touch. Indeed if the gas fill pressure is too high, the tube temperature can reach the glass melting point. This results in an implosion that looks like a reverse tubulation. The influx of outside air through the hole quickly destroys the tube.

Because the electrons follow a narrow path, they repeatedly strike the electrodes at the same point. Overtime the metal shell breaks down emitting metal atoms into the tube. The metal atoms deposit on the glass wall near the electrodes blackening and weakening the glass. Eventually, the tube or the electrode fails resulting in tube burnout.

Another light lasing technique causes an intense light beam in only one spot within the tube. This is done by shrinking the tube interior diameter before processing. This way the path of electrons is forced into a narrow path brightening the beam at this point.

Shrink a tube interior by rotating the tube with a flame focused at a single point. As the tube shrinks, gather the glass trying to maintain the tube exterior diameter. Watch the tube interior diameter as it shrinks. Do not allow the tube interior to collapse.

When the interior has shrunk to the desired diameter, roll the tube back and forth across the table. Gently blow to keep it open while rounding and evening the tube exterior. Leave the tube in one spot to cool evenly. This may take up to half an hour depending on the amount of glass gathered in the restriction. Then keep flame away from this point or dangerous shattering may occur. The thick glass insulates the interior glass molecules from temperature change. With sudden temperature change, strain is caused as the exterior molecules expand against the more rigid interior molecules causing explosive breakage.

Single Electrode Tubes

A typical neon unit is lit by a high voltage, low current, sixty-cycle transformer. The electricity changes direction sixty times each second–an electrode is positively charged thirty times a second then negatively charged thirty times a second.

By increasing the frequency, the gas atoms light much easier. High frequency transformers are rated twenty thousand to one hundred fifty thousand cycles instead of the conventional sixty cycles. Because the gas illuminates easily at these frequencies, it is possible to light a tube with only one electrode. To complete the circuit to ground, electrical energy travels through conductive molecules in air surrounding the tube. Single electrode tubes brighten when touched

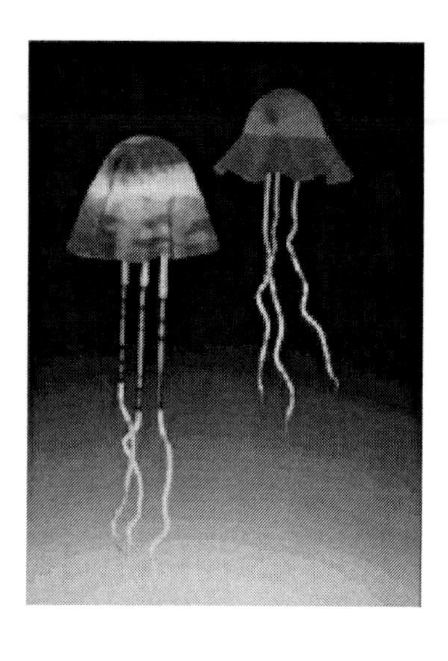

because the body acts like an antennae, a conduit drawing more electrical current through the tube.

Figure 15-2
Single electrode "Jellyfish"
(Eric Ehlenberger Studios)

Inert gases are most electrically efficient at very low pressures. Neon gas is most electrically efficient at pressure less than one millimeter of mercury. Yet, the reason typical gassing charts do not recommend this low pressure is due to sputtering, electrode breakdown, and luminosity. Gassing charts attempt to strike a balance between both sputtering and luminosity. However, a single electrode tube operates best between one-third and one-half recommended fill pressure. This is because sputtering is less likely to occurr at the low operating current level produced by a single electrode transformer.

Figure 15-3
Tipping-off the extra electrode on a single electrode unit

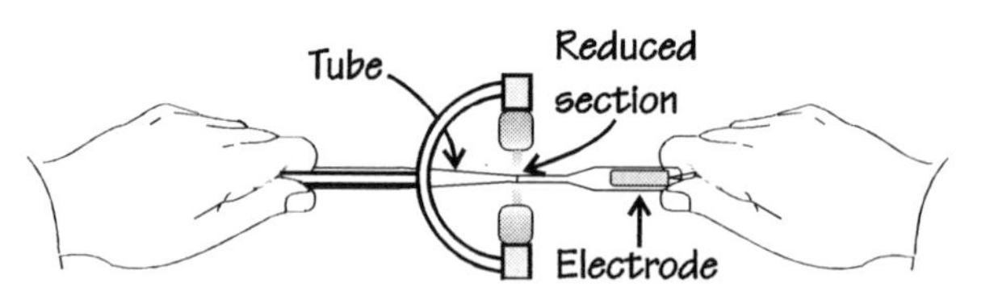

Processing a single electrode tube can be challenging. One simple method uses two electrodes during processing, like a normal neon unit. The extraneous electrode is removed after aging. To facilitate removal of the electrode, reduce to five or six millimeters an area between the unit and the extra electrode. Make the reduced section by stretching the tube or by welding in a length of five or six millimeter tubing.

A more complicated single electrode unit, like a multi-limbed tree, is processed differently. Following through with the previous example, weld the electrodes in-line with the largest part of the unit, the tree trunk. Normal bombarding heats the trunk but the branch tubes are heated with a heat gun during evacuation. Further impurities are freed by gently running a spark coil over the branch tubes during evacuation. Not all impurities need be removed from a single electrode tube as with a sign tube. Single electrode low operating current discourages electrode sputter, liberation and lighting of impurities.

Another method used to purify a single electrode tube is to heat the unit in an oven. This way, the entire glass sculpture heats evenly. A small opening made in the oven allows connection between the vacuum pump and the tube. However, this method does not allow proper emitter coating conversion since the electrode never reaches conversion temperature. So, use an uncoated electrode or an induction coil designed to heat the electrode to proper temperature.

Terminating Ends

There are several ways to terminate a single electrode tube. The end can be made pointed, flat, round or even square. Heating the tube and gently stretching the glass to separation makes a pointed end. But the resulting tiny tip is fragile and sharp. So, to strengthen it and make it safer to handle, immediately upon separation, fire polish the end.

To make a flat end, rotate the tube end in a flame until it seals. Then press the molten end gently onto a flat surface and blow a little air into the tube to prevent collapse. After flattening, rotate the tube sides against a table to help keep the tube edge round then finally anneal.

1. Heat
2. Stretch
3. Cut
4. Seal
Point

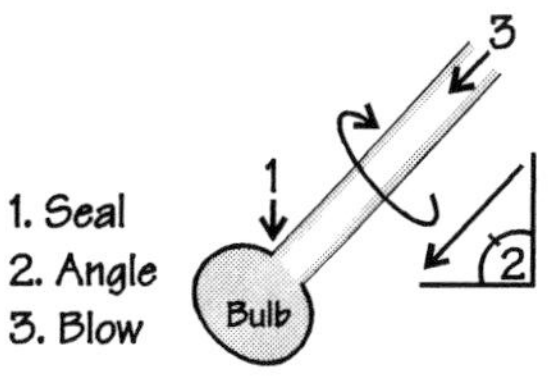

Figure 15-4 Pointed and bulbous ends

A large diameter tube wall needs thinning before flattening. This is done by stretching and cooling the tube then cutting the middle of the stretch before sealing and shaping. Thinning the glass wall lessens chance for strain to develop.

Make a bulbous end by rotating the tube end in a flame shrinking the tube diameter. Continue heating until it closes and seals. Remove the tube from the flame, point it downward and blow into the tube while rotating. Blow until the desired size and shape develop then let it cool. A bulbous end lights very dimly. This is due to thinning electric current density; the light spreads throughout the bulb.

Obviously, a neatly squared end is difficult to make in a round tube. Nevertheless, to try, seal the tube end by rotating and collapsing in a flame. Quickly push the molten end into a small, box shaped form then blow into the tube. Remove the tube from the form and let cool. Or alternatively, flatten the sealed end on the table then press the sides between two blocks. Quickly rotate the tube one-quarter turn and press again. Keep air pressure in the tube to help control distortion.

Bubble Blowing

To blow a glass bubble in a length of tubing, first gather the glass to insure final wall thickness. Do this by rotating the tube in a flame, slowly pushing the tube inward. Try to keep the gathered glass evenly heated and centered along the tube axis. Remove the tube from the flame and blow in increments all the while rotating and gently pushing inward. Slight pushing rounds the bubble while pulling elongates it. Excessive pushing or pulling amplifies these effects. Excessive gathering creates a ring around a sphere. Often, a mix of movements are needed.

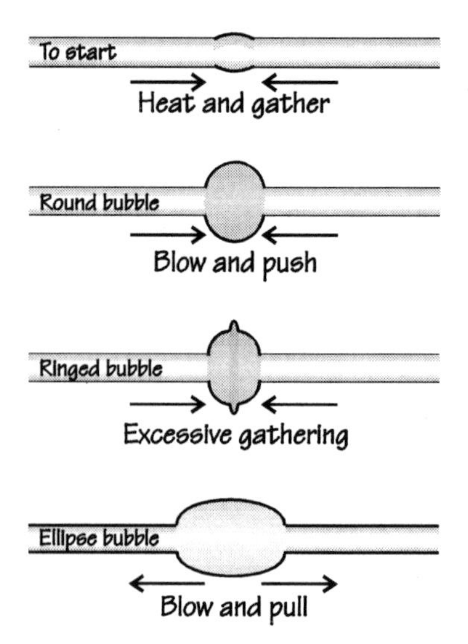

Figure 15-5 Blowing glass bubbles

Make multi-colored glass bubbles by welding various colored tubes together then blowing a sphere between the welds. Mix soda and lead glass tubes for more color choices. Mix patterned coated tubes with neon gas and mercury vapor or add crackle or lasing effects for even more variation.

European Bends

European neon glassblowers seldom bend glass like in the United States. They often cut and weld glass at angles to form changes of direction. Neon artists use this technique to form unique looking turns. To form a ninety-degree change of direction using the European style, make a forty-five degree cut through a tube. Do this by laying the tube on a block and hold the file edge forty-five degrees to the tube. Off the block, cut the tube about one-third the way around then pull apart. Position the two angled ends such that a ninety-degree angle is formed and weld together without losing the distinct shape.

Art Mounting Methods

Mounting a neon tube for art purposes is an art itself. Using standard sign hardware and mounting methods results in unwanted sign like appearance. Other materials and techniques are better suited for art and creative thinking sometimes even shopping is necessary.

Wall hung signs are usually bolted to a wall or hung with chain. The bolts or chain pass through the sign backing usually made of metal or acrylic. However, to hang neon art, consider fastening picture wire to the back of the piece. Picture wire is an accepted standard for hanging many other types of art: paintings, photographs, wall sculptures, etcetera. To hang a neon piece, fasten small, drilled angle irons to the back of a metal or wood piece or securely glue drilled acrylic blocks to an acrylic art piece. Position them on the back where the piece will hang flush and balanced against a wall. Pass the wire through the holes, loop and securely twist around itself several times.

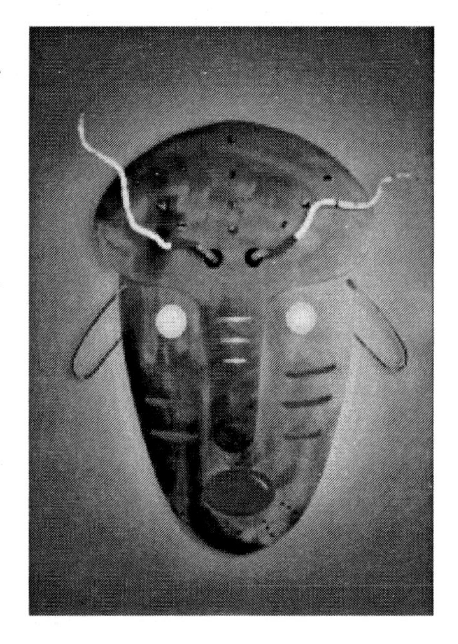

Figure 15-6 "Mask" neon art wall piece (Eric Ehlenberger Studios)

Mount tubes to a wall piece using a minimum of visible support. Tasteful looking tube supports are available at your sign supply distributor. But also consider wrapping a tube behind the backing then attach the tube to the backing using several nylon zip ties and their accompanying self-stick bases. This way, the tube is fully supported out of sight. Also, consider terminating tube ends behind the backing. This helps hide electrodes, insulators and wiring too.

Freestanding art is mounted many ways. Prefabricated bases are available through sign supply houses and specialty markets. They come in various shapes and sizes and with or without transformer. Homemade bases are made from hobby boxes and ceramic pots. Any art piece should be labeled with a sticker stating in one-quarter inch or bigger letters the words "High Voltage" and any other safety suggestions.

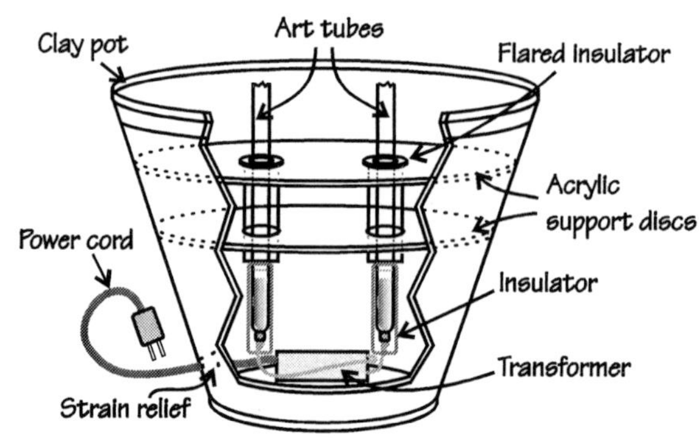

Figure 15-7 Homemade freestanding base

Special Effect Transformers

Recent advances in solid state transformers have added to the neon artist palette a series of special effects: tracing, field lighting, bead making, flashing or sequencing.

Tracers or spellers, as they are called, light the tube from one end to the other tracing the tube path. These transformers offer a variable trace rate so the tube will trace at different speeds. Usually, the tube traces once, shuts off momentarily and then begins again. But some transformers trace forward and backward appearing to fill then unfill the tube with light.

Field lighting transformers light a tube with no electrodes and no wires. The power supply creates a high frequency electric field exciting fill gas atoms to luminous levels. Because the field is weak, so is the light output. Hence, most field lit art is best-viewed in very dim spaces and often are made only to photograph.

Bead making transformers establish waveforms throughout a tube. Where the wave peaks align, they join energy creating a bright band of light. Where the wave peaks oppose, the energy cancels and no light is produced. This creates beads of light within the tube. Some transformers even produce variable speed moving beads of light.

Flashing neon is not new. Mechanical flashers have been around since the early days of neon. Most interrupt the primary side of the transformer; others interrupt the high voltage, secondary side. Today, solid state circuits replace their mechanical counterparts with manufacturers building flash circuitry into tiny, lightweight transformers making the effect affordable and easy to offer even in art.

Some flashers, called sequencers, light one tube then another. A bank of transformers controlled by a sequencer is used to create neon animation. A single, solid state transformer with a sequencer built-in simplifies installation. However, always check local sign codes before offering a flashing sign or art piece. Some local authorities have strict guidelines governing their usage.

Pricing Neon Art

The application of neon as an art is limited only by the artist's imagination. With more tube colors, mounting materials and special effect transformers coming to market each year, the future appears bright indeed. Nevertheless, pricing custom work is difficult, even vague. But because the work is original and uses cutting-edge materials and techniques, the price also should be unique. So, charge more for neon artwork than for neon signs as this market bears far higher prices.

Figure 15-8 Mixed media wall piece close up (Eric Ehlenberger Studios)

Figure 15-9
It's the human touch
(www.freeimages.co.uk)

Articles

The following articles appeared in *Sign Builder Illustrated Magazine*. Some have been edited and terms are not included in Index.

Tips for the Neon Newbie

All neon craftsmen were a beginner once. Some of us were lucky and had access to those willing to share tips and techniques. Others relied on a book or video and trained themselves the hard way.

Over the past ten years a wealth of information has come forth for the neon neophyte in the form of schools, books, videos and websites; there's never been a better time to learn. So, in the spirit of sharing, I offer these tidbits to help the neon newbie circumvent common beginner troubles.

Nuisance Wounds

First the obvious, burns and cuts. Making neon involves heating glass to about twelve hundred degrees Fahrenheit in a flame-throwing burner. And the glass stays hot to the touch for several minutes. So, burns are a painful and inevitable part of learning.

Keeping track of the tube length most recently worked is the key to avoiding most skin burns. Ironically, it's usually the balance point of the work and hence the most natural point to pick up a tube.

The difference between a mild burn and a severe one is related to the length of time your skin is in contact with the heated tube. And because the brain takes a fraction of a second to determine whether a change is hot or cold more time is allotted to burn.

So to avoid injury, sense temperature change quickly. Touch a tube and if you feel a change, release the tube at once, even if the change is cold. This way you minimize contact time and potential burn severity.

When burns occur, treat with ointment, some use aloe vera, and then cover with a bandage. Obviously the ointment aids healing. The bandage will help insulate the sensitive area from heat that splashes from the burners. This will make continuing work more comfortable.

Cuts - Yikes! Sometimes they are more painful than burns. The best way to avoid a cut is to keep the work area clean. This is because most cuts occur from tiny glass shards left on the worktable caused during tube cutting.

These tiny glass fragments find their way into your skin when you lean on them or worse, when you brush them away with your hand. So, vacuum or sweep the work area regularly to keep the table free of the little weapons.

Cuts also happen when pushing a cork into a tube end. If the end is not cut evenly, a glass spike hangs out there like a dagger waiting for a target. That's when your finger comes along and pushes into it.

The only way to avoid this accident is to check the end before inserting the cork. If that's inconvenient, partially insert the cork then press it fully into the tube by pushing it against the table. This way if a glass dagger waits, it jabs into the table and not your finger.

Molten Breakdowns

Another common rookie problem is not heating the glass sufficiently to work into a proper bend. Molten glass is unwieldy so the problem isn't without merit.

Still to form a strong, smooth bend and have enough time to adjust the bent tube to a pattern, you must heat a length until it shrinks in diameter and glows. This requires control.

Control is best learned by simply heating a straight tube in a flame until you lose said control. That is, heat a length of tube to molten then continue heating with no intention of forming a bend.

Do this until the glass is so unwieldy you must stop the exercise or the tube collapses on itself. After umpteen efforts, return to practicing bends and see the results controlled molten glass offers.

Flipping Matters

Neon patterns get flipped over, mirror image, before bending glass to them. This is so the finished sign is flat across the front. When one forgets to flip the pattern, the finished product reads backward like a mirror image.

I recall one student who on her hurried last day of training made such a mistake. Her sign was to be used to advertise a business opening. During mounting, she let out a yelp. Her pattern had not been reversed and now her completed sign was reversed by this error, as was her usual chipper attitude.

Her unique and temporary solution was creative to say the least. She mounted the sign just below a lofty window such that a properly aligned mirror reflected the sign correctly oriented.

If you want to avoid forced reflective mounting, always remember to flip the finished pattern over before bending glass to it.

Blowhose Woes

Forget the cork or blowhose and usually you can kiss the formation of a bend goodbye. Bent, molten glass requires a puff of air to round out the tube; its function is really two fold, for aesthetics and mechanics. For a bend that doesn't get blown-out is both unattractive and likely weakened.

Okay, so even the seasoned glass blower forgets a cork or blowhose once-and-awhile. The key is not to panic. If it’s time to bend and you discover a missing blowhose, simply form the bend then puff into the open tube end.

If a blowhose is intact but no cork seals the opposite end, simply plug it with a finger and blow. The result may be of questionable quality or appearance but often this quick trick averts a complete project restart.

The best check to ensure a sealed connection is to puff quick and hard into the tube before entering the flame, make it a habit. If the tube blows back, you're sealed and ready to work. Make this tip a custom and never forget the blowhose or cork again.

Put your tongue over the mouthpiece while heating a tube. Go ahead, it'll be fun. Not! Air trapped inside a tube expands as it is heated and so does the glass tube if the expanding air has no place to displace; it's like corking both ends of the tube.

A tongue-in-cheek solution is to breathe through your mouth past the mouthpiece. It positions your tongue in its cradle at the bottom of your mouth, away from the mouthpiece end. This allows expanding air to displace and averts the problem. It gives your tongue a rest too.

So, Get On With It

Okay you neon newbies, stand at your post and take command of that tube with these hot little tidbits. You'll still suffer that occasional cut or burn, that unwieldy bend, backward tube and forgotten cork. But at least now you can say, like the rest of us, that you knew better.

Self-Training #1

Learning to make neon is like learning anything else with one big difference. It's more difficult. I know - I know, that's a pretty bold statement. But I've heard it repeated many times and from many sources including an orthopedic surgeon!

And it's not like all I've ever done is neon, not true. I was an ASE certified auto mechanic for many years; I managed a couple small businesses; I earned an AS in Physics; I wrote three books and became a columnist for SBI; I am a Certified Computer Service Technician and I recently completed three screenplays - anyone from Hollywood reading this? Whew, where was I when all this happened!

Enough of the "I's." My point is learning neon glass blowing was the most difficult pill I've ever ingested. Well, except for divorce - but that's another article. So, don't expect training yourself will be easy because it won't be. But it will be fun, in-between cuts and burns, and it will be most rewarding.

Finding Resources

The best way to learn neon is through professional training that uses a certified or agency approved course outline. Many states approve training programs but vary in qualification standards: some expect pure professionalism, others expect only to collect a fee. So, it's buyer beware.

This article is for those with no choice but to train themselves. So first, know that you are not a pioneer; others have successfully earned the title of Neon Glassblower all by themselves.

Here's how to begin. Buy books, buy videos, and subscribe to trade magazines, order any information offered that you could comfortably afford remembering that you'll need to purchase equipment too.

Now, read all you can and watch those videos but don't expect to learn everything in one week. Instead, get comfortable with terms used in the trade (every trade has its own language) and with how working molten glass appears.

Going Mad

When it's time to buy equipment, don't worry about purchasing tube-processing equipment right away. I know how exciting it is to light your first tube. But it will take time before your practice tubes are worthy or even capable of lighting. Besides, tube processing is the mad scientist end of neon.

All right, you've learned some basic terms, you've watched someone work glass in a flame, and you've setup your glass bending equipment. Now, where to start?

Getting Started

Here is what I suggest, start with a basic skill; learn to cut glass tubing. It sounds easy but isn't and you must become consistent and proficient if you are ever to build a sign.

The glass file is a mill-bastard type. Use it by holding it at a forty-five degree angle to the tube. Draw the file edge back and forth with sawing like motion. The goal is to create an etch one-third to one-half the way around a tube so rotate the tube under the file. The etch causes a strain within the glass that separates the tube cleanly, hopefully.

The etch itself seldom parts the tube. Usually, you have to pull on the tube or tap it gently behind the etch to encourage separation. If you've ever watched a journeyman cut a series of glass tubes in rapid succession, you know it looks easy. But you just try it.

Working In Fire

After learning to cut tubes successfully - the tube parts and the ends are flush - it's time to practice sticking them back together by welding. I'll assume your burners operate properly and you know how to light and adjust them. If you don't, there's more frustrating lessons to learn.

Begin by inserting a cork in one tube end and your blowhose in another tube. I suggest you use a blowhose for safety and use clear tubing first for simplicity.

Hold the tube by your fingertips, palms up and position the smoothly cut ends near the tip of a properly adjusted flame. Rotate the tubes one-quarter turn every second or so until both ends glow equally. They should appear soft but not dripping.

Once heated, stop rotating and gently touch the molten ends together. Do this inside or outside the flame, outside might be easier at first.

Once joined, insert the seam directly into the flame center and rotate the tube one-quarter turn every second or two to evenly heat the seam. Do this until it glows evenly and shrinks slightly in diameter.

To work the seam, blend the glass, use one of the listed methods:

1.) Gently suck-in then, blow out the tube. Do this until the glass begins to stiffen then heat and work several more times.
2.) Twist the joined tubes in opposite directions until blended.
3.) Repeatedly push the ends together then pull to the proper diameter.
4.) Use a combination of these methods.

Work the seam until it is airtight and smooth in appearance. You can test the seal by blowing hard into the tube just as it stiffens. It should blow back just a little.

In grand finale, heat the weld one last time to near molten then quickly lie it on the worktable and straighten. This final heating helps remove strain from within the glass structure. Strain builds over time and can cause a tube to crack or shatter; it is obviously undesirable.

Making the Turns --- The L-bend
In the beginning, practice making basic bends freehand, without a pattern. Once comfortable, draw a series of bends and practice forming the bend to the pattern.

The first bend for the self-taught to practice, is the L-bend, a ninety-degree turn. As with all bends, a particular length of tubing requires heating to form it without thinning the glass wall. For L-bends, this length is about twice the diameter of the tube. So, heat twenty millimeters of glass on a ten-millimeter tube, thirty millimeters on a fifteen-millimeter diameter tube, etcetera.

Use two marks to indicate this length then divide it with a center mark. The center mark is where you'll form the crease inside the bend.

Start by heating this length evenly. Move the tube back and forth through a properly adjusted flame. Rotate it one-quarter turn every three or five passes. Do this until the tube glows and the tube diameter shrinks slightly.

Then point the marks toward the ceiling and raise both hands simultaneously in an arch forty-five degrees. This splits the workload evenly and causes the molten glass to flow smoothly. Finally, puff into the tube, preferably via a blowhose, then set the bend flat on the table and block flat once. Let it cool.

Forming a smooth, useable L-bend is harder than it looks or sounds. And making a series of consistent, useable bends is the secret to mastering neon glassblowing. Now guess what it takes to make a series of useable bends. That's right... practice!

The U-bend
The U-bend is a one hundred-eighty degree turn. Because it forms a larger turn than an L-bend, the U-bend requires more tubing be heated to molten. So mark then evenly heat two and one-half to three times the tube diameter.

Once molten, point the marks to the ceiling and move your hands upward until your fingertips almost touch. Let the outside marks pivot in space positioning the center mark in the bend middle. This motion causes the glass to flow smoothly aligned with gravity. Finally, blow to fullness, set down and block flat.

The Offset
The Offset is a three-dimensional bend used to represent a sharp angle, one too sharp physically to bend successfully in glass.

Mark the Offset then heat and bend just like the U-bend with one important difference, angle the tubes in opposite directions on either side of the bend. Form the U-shape then push one tube away and pull the other toward you. Blow the bend out to the correct diameter and set down sideways, one tube flat upon the table and the other resting upon a suitable block.

The Drop or Raise

The Drop or Raise is simply a change of elevation, one block high, and a change of direction, usually ninety-degrees. Like the Offset, it is a three-dimensional bend too. A Drop and Raise combination is often used to form "jumps" between letters.

To form a Raise, mark and heat slightly more glass than the height of the block used to support the finished bend. Once molten, drop the tube in one hand one block height keeping both tubes parallel to the floor. Angle the tubes the desired direction then blow. Often, forming a Raise or Drop includes a slight roll of one tube. This gets complicated so I recommend researching this combination bend before practicing it.

Troubleshooting and More

It's easy for things to go wrong when bending neon and troubleshooting is illustrated only in some books and videos. But developing trouble-shooting skills helps you fix a stinker bend while working and before it's too late. So, to become proficient, discover these troubleshooting skills and develop them.

Well, it looks like you've got plenty to keep you busy until the next self-teaching article: Making block and script letters. Happy bending.

Self-Training #2

You've committed to teaching yourself neon. You've purchased books and started reading, watched videos, and read my previous articles. Now, you're comfortable with neon glassblowing basics: making Welds, L-bends, U-bends, Offsets, and Drops-n-Raises. What's next?

Patterns and Reversals

Putting the basics together to form letters is next. But first, we need to make a pattern. And you need to know this, all neon sign patterns are reversed prior to bending. This is so that the sign face ultimately is flat.

Draw a Block letter A on paper then tube it in. "Tube it in" means all lines, all strokes are denoted as a tube. Once drawn, flip the pattern over and transfer to bending material. Or, if you prefer, place metal screen over the flipped paper pattern and work that way.

Whichever method you use, make habit of flipping the paper pattern over whether your design requires it or not. Consider the Block letter A: it is symmetrical and doesn't really require flipping. But flip it anyway and develop the habit now so future errors are less likely.

Straight-line Block Letters

It's time to put your basic skills to the test and make Block letters in glass. I recommend practicing these straight-line Block letters first - A,E,H,K,M,X- then move on to curved letters. This way, you continue developing basic bend skills and their variations.

Other Block Letters are easily derived from the suggested practice letters: the F from the E, the serif I from the H, and the W from the M, etcetera.

Usually, it's best to form the inside of a letter first. This way you don't bend yourself into a corner, you avoid overlapping tubes.

To bend the A, make the shallow angled L-bend first. Then Doubleback, a U-bend on its side, over the top then lastly Drop back onto the table. In three moves, the inside of the A is complete and you're ready to continue forming the letter.

Basic Bend Variations
Continue by forming a V-bend at the top of the A. But then you say, I've never practiced making the V-bend. No, you didn't practice it. But the V-bend is simply a variation of the L-bend; it's a sharper turn. Just make the bend center mark nearer the letter top rather than the inside corner as with L-bends.

If you've gotten this far, practice making connection bends at the letter ends. These bends connect one letter to another and most often are Offsets and variations of Raises. Again, look to signs and illustrations for examples.

Once you've completed several Block letters, practice welding them together using the crossor cannon fire. Also, practice using a handtorch to weld. Large unwieldy units are pieced together this way.

After making several consistent A's, try making the E. Again, begin bending the inside first then work outward.

Many letters require use of slight variations of basic bends like the V-bend. Consider the Leaning Raise used to form the H. The Leaning Raise is made exactly like a Raise except the bend is left leaning to one side. It is not rolled, aligned vertically. Eliminate the roll motion during bending to carry out the lean.

The subsequent Doubleback under the Leaning Raise forms a bend that resembles a Doubleback-Drop combination and that's exactly what it is. The advantage making the combination this way, rather than the routine reverse, is that the opportunity to stick glass together when making the Drop is eliminated.

Curved Block Letters
Once you've nearly mastered straight-line Block letters, try curved Block letters. Curves require use of the ribbon burner. To evenly heat a tube in a ribbon burner simply rotate the tube methodically or flip it back and forth heating at least two sides of the tube equally.

Now comes a variation of the rule, bend the inside first. Whenever possible make a ribbon curve that aids formation of the letter inside first. Do this because this curve is often the most visible or is the largest bend in the letter. Getting it right makes a better-looking letter.

Consider practicing the letters -B,G,O,R,S- because most other letter are easily formed from these. Practicing these letters hones your basic skills and prepares you to learn script letters. See there really is method to this madness.

Script Letters
Script letters are made mostly of curves formed in the ribbon burner. To make a good-looking script sign you need to form smooth curves and transitions between them. Hopefully, bending many curved Block letters will benefit this effort.

This is worth mentioning again, if there's an inside to a letter bend it first. But if there's a ribbon curve that aids this function, make it first.

Consider the bending sequence for the Script letter E. We begin by forming an inside curve then work our way out. We bend in a planned sequence that eliminates the possibility of crossed tubes.

Size Matters
The size of a letter can affect how you bend it. If the E is about two to four inches in height; you may attempt to form bends 1, 3 and 4 in one maneuver (see page 94). Simply elevating the tube flat onto a block eliminates bend number 2, making bend number 1 a slow, smooth drop onto the table.

To aid forming the sharp turn at bend 3, preheat it a few seconds before heating the entire length to molten. Preheating warms this section of tubing to higher temperature thus causing it to bend more, form a sharper turn.

The same is true when bending the Script letter O. If the letter is large; the bends are easiest to form in the sequence shown on page 96. If it is small, bends 1, 2 and 3 can be formed in a single heat provided bend number 2 is preheated sufficiently.

Consistency
Of course, bending several consistent and smooth script letters requires much practice. Yet there is reward, Block letters will now seem simple to bend by comparison. See there's that method to madness thing again.

Practice making a few individual script letters then draw a complete script word like "Open" or "Best Deal." Practice making the letters individually then weld them together.

Eventually, try making two or more script letters in series, on the same stick of tubing. When you can plan this task properly then pull it off in glass, you know you're well on your way to becoming a journeyman Block and Script letter neon glassblower.

Self-Training #3

Congratulations if you've made it this far training yourself, because most folks don't. And it's unfortunate because after a few more glass bending challenges then diving off into the mad scientist end of neon, tube processing, the lucrative side of neon can become a reality.

So, what's on the agenda this glass-blowing lesson? How about making large circles, border tubes, multiple outline units and bubbles. Your glass bending experience to date should help make these lessons a manageable and fun task.

The Big O

The Big O or Large Circle is a challenging glass exercise. Because the curve is so slight on a circle three feet or larger in diameter, the tube cannot be heated as molten as usual. Too hot a tube sags with gravity more than indicated on the pattern.

Because the tube is heated so slight, strain usually develops within the glass structure, strain that eventually leads to breakage. You make a cut on your perfect curve and a split begins traveling around your masterpiece. Sometimes the split travels the full length of the curve ruining your effort. What to do?

There are a couple solutions. One is to heat the glass to molten and allow it to sag excessively with gravity. Just prior to exiting the flame, flip the tube over so you have a second or two to get the tube to the pattern before it sags too much. You can pull on the tube slightly to remove excess sag also.

At the pattern, make certain straight tubing remains tangent to the curve. That is, no straight tubing runs along the curve, it stays outside it. The extra heating reduces chance of strain and by remaining tangent to the curve, chances of flat spots or wobbles are diminished.

Another solution is to flame anneal the tube. Many craftsmen return the tube to the flame after forming the curve and after the glass has setup a moment. They heat the curve backside a few seconds to slow the cooling rate. This effectively reduces chance of strain. But even this method requires practice so expect some disappointments.

Don't make very large circles from a single tube. Break them up into segments to ease bending, tube processing and handling. And don't be afraid to use a jig, a piece of curved wood or even tiny nails driven around the pattern. Many craftsmen use jigs to speed up production.

Neon Border Tubes

Border tubes are simply tubes that border something: usually a building, window or wall. The challenge making them is the border tube needs to be extremely straight and the tube ends must be accurately formed.

Border tube electrodes often are connected so they align head-on or side-by-side requiring a high degree of accuracy when forming. With some fixed insulators, improperly aligned electrodes result in breakage during installation. So, getting the bends right the first time saves everyone a little grief.

Practice making border tube ends using two to three inch pieces of sealed scrap clear tubing. Using scrap glass will save expense over using real electrodes potentially destroyed during practice. Weld them on in a crossor cannon fire. This will aid your skills for the next maneuver, forming the connecting bend.

Most border tubes run about eight feet to twelve feet in length. Since glass tubes commonly are four-feet in length, this means you'll be making plenty of very straight welds.

To aid keeping the tube straight, align it over a straight line drawn directly on the bending table. Some prefer to eyeball the tube straight and other craftsman build a jig to keep it aligned while they weld with a handtorch. Any method practical for you is the right method.

Double Outline

Bending double outline letters or designs offers unique challenges. But for the most part, double outline is easier to bend than most specialty letter styles.

Planning is most important so, remember the first rule of bending: bend the inside first then bend outward. The rule still holds true with one additional observation. Look for a basic bend, an L-bend, U-bend or Offset that you can save out of sequence for folding a complicated piece together.

Folding a double outline piece together using a saved basic bend is a powerful tool that will save you both time and frustration. It will save time because you won't need to make so many cuts and welds. It will save frustration because you'll be more productive and produce a more attractive product.

Sometimes it is useful to save more than one bend out of sequence; it always depends upon the design. But by choosing to save easy to form basic bends, you increase your chance of success.

Channel Letters

Channel Letters are big multiple outline letters. They're used to illuminate plastic or metal cans made in the shape of letters or designs.

Channel letters tubes are bent much the same as double outline letters except that they are usually made of larger diameter tubing. Large diameter tubes offer less electrical resistance than do small diameter tubes. So, any given transformer can drive more linear tubing.

Manufacturing a tube that runs much more than ten to fifteen linear feet is difficult to process and unwieldy to handle. So, break multiple outline designs into smaller, more manageable segments and make your work and that of other's less demanding.

Glass Bubbles

You won't find much use for glass bubbles in conventional neon signs but you might in neon artwork.

First, be aware that large glass bubbles light much more dimly than the rest of a tube because light spreads across the surface decreasing light density. Also be aware that it's important to gather glass before blowing it into a bubble. This helps maintain glass wall thickness.

Add these bending skills to your bag of tricks and you'll find any new glass challenge obtainable. But keep in mind, every project is unique.

Self-Training #4

Finally, the moment you've waited for, assuming you actually waited: tube processing and lighting your neon tube. Yes, this is the mad-scientist and fun side of neon though some find it a little frightening.

The Mad Scientist - You

Tube processing is mad-scientist like because you work with high voltage electricity, high vacuum technology and gaseous elements that light in colors - neat stuff and the reason it's so Frankensteinien fun.

But it's also scary because now you discover how worthy your work is. Will your tube hold a vacuum? Will it break under electro-mechanical, high vacuum and heat stress? Can you work safely and comfortably with high voltage electricity? Let's explore and find out.

Safety

First and foremost is safety. You're working with ten thousand to twenty thousand volts of electricity and pumping between one-quarter to one and one-quarter amps through the tube. That's enough juice to kill you and a horse.

And you can cause permanent damage to tissues like your lungs and nervous system if you don't take the necessary precautions when working with high vacuum and liquid mercury.

All possible safety concerns are beyond the scope of this article. So, <u>Follow All Manufacturers' Safety Precautions</u> when using their equipment or product! And if you don't understand something, research it first. The risks to your safety are that great.

Generic Tube Processing Step-by-Step

The following method of tube processing should be considered broad in scope and generic. It uses the simplest of equipment and the most basic technique. It assumes you understand pumping theory, equipment and material safety and use.

1) Attach the neon unit to the manifold. The manifold will provide the passage for removal of impurities inside the unit and passage for pure inert gas to fill it. If you're using argon in the unit, make certain you

attach a mercury trap containing a drop of mercury between the unit and manifold.

2) Insert mica between tight bends. The electrical voltage used to bombard a tube is powerful enough to blow clean through your work. Mica will add electrical resistance and discourage blow through.

3) Connect the bombarding transformer leads to each electrode and attach a temperature indicator to the tube.

4) Open the vacuum valve and reduce pressure in the tube. Use of a vacuum gauge is recommended but a minimalist's alternative is to pump the unit for a few minutes then measure using simple butyl gauge a couple millimeters air into the unit.

5) Activate the bombarding transformer; the tube should light. If a leak is present, search for it using a spark coil and repair. Assuming no leaks are present, slowly increase current flow according the electrode manufacturer's suggestions.

6) When the tube dims or flickers, make a pass with the vacuum valve as needed to keep the tube lit. A vacuum gauge is a better indicator of when and how much vacuum to apply.

7) Maintain balance between vacuum and electrical current until the tube reaches a temperature around four hundred twenty-five degrees Fahrenheit, about the burning point of dry paper.

8) Next, process the electrodes according to manufacturer's instructions. This usually involves increasing both current and level of vacuum. This operation heats the electrode shell to cherry red and converts a protective chemical coating.

9) Once the electrodes are processed, allow the vacuum pump time to remove hot impure gasses, usually a few minutes or so. A quick check to see if the tube is ready to fill with inert gas is to close the vacuum valve then "bump" the bombarding switch. The tube should not light, as no remaining gases are present. If it does light, chances are good a leak exists in the tube or in the pumping system.

10) If the tube is comfortable to touch, it's probably cool enough to fill with inert gas. Avoid filling too hot a tube as it results in low final pressure, cool gas exerts less pressure than hot gas. Use a chart to determine the appropriate fill pressure then add the correct gas, most often neon or argon.

11) Once filled, "bump" the bombarding switch and check for proper color. Neon should light brilliant red-orange and argon dim lavender.

12) Now safely remove all mica, wires and indicators from the tube. If filled with neon, gently heat a point on the tubulation tube near the unit or on the manifold side of the mercury trap if an argon unit. Even a filled tube is under vacuum relative to atmospheric pressure and so easily seals closed once heated to molten. Avoid glass build-up at the seal-off point or the glass may strain, crack then leak. Do this by quickly peeling the unit away once the tubulation tube begins to collapse. Follow the unit with the torch.

13) Now burn-in the unit. Let it run on a slightly oversized transformer until its color stabilizes and no other problems develop. Some shops burn-in a tube for only fifteen minutes. Others burn-in a unit for eight hours or longer. Longer burn-in times can assure fewer tube troubles after installation.

14) If the unit is an argon/mercury tube, let the electrodes cool to room temperature then roll the droplet of mercury through the tube covering each electrode. Finally, burn-in again until the tube is bright mercury blue in color.

Not Finished Yet

These are the minimum steps used to process a tube. But before the tube goes out the door, there's more work to be done.

Blockout all appropriate tube lengths including any connection tubes between letters, electrodes and the bends they're connected to, essentially any tube that should not be visibly lit. I've actually seen new neon signs installed with no tubes blocked-out and wondered why anyone paid for the sign; it was barely legible.

Once properly blocked-out, mount and insulate as needed according to local codes. Yes, neon installation codes sometimes varies region to region, even city to city. So, before mounting or installing any neon tube, discover and conform to local authority rules that govern your neon sign.

This article series was offered as one possible course outline for the self-trained neon craftsman. Though there is no substitute for hands-on training under a journeyman tradesman, many wannabes will never get that chance. Even so, realize this: an honest journeyman craftsman will admit that after years of glassblowing there are always new lessons to be learned and at some point even they become self-taught.

Top 10 Must-Haves

What is the Top 10 Must-Haves? It's my list of favorite ten elements to incorporate into a neon shop. I'm talking tangible elements over which we have control. Not intangibles like always having friendly customers, or a wonderfully giving boss or overwhelmingly admiring coworkers though those are nice elements too.

I'm talking about physical elements that maximize productivity, comfort and reduce stress. You know, make the job a better life experience all around. Now, on any given day, any one of these favorites could shift up or down a notch depending upon one's mood. That of course, is every tubebender's option. So, with this understanding, let's move on to the countdown:

10) Music.

Tunes help keep to a minimum those over-critical voices that sometimes hammer inside our heads. They can also keep one from worrying about plummeting stock prices or midriff bulge among other things. In doing so, music helps increase our concentration.

Music also can set tempo, develop rhythm of movement that aids even heating of the glass. Naturally, it helps to choose suitable music to maximize the benefit. So, consider classical, concert, folk, rock, jazz, even conga music if you think it might help.

9) Supplies and tool placement.

Strolling across the shop to collect electrodes and glass is sometimes all it takes to break that tubebender groove we occasionally achieve. That little trip opens the door to interruptions from co-workers, customers and other distractions too.

So, keep all necessary materials close to the work bench to stave off such circumstance. Keep close by electrodes, glass tubing, spare corks, pencils and files, even a thermos of coffee or other drink - anything that might unnecessarily drag you away from that bench.

8) Jigs.

Jigs increase bending accuracy and make work less strenuous. Consider using jigs when bending lengthy, slow curves or when welding long straight border tubes. Homemade jigs almost guarantee bending accuracy and thus reduce craftsman stress. I hope reducing job stress is what this decade is remembered for.

7) Multiple patterns and tools.
When mass-producing neon units use multiple patterns and glassblowing tools. This lessens the number of burner adjustments and time spent waiting for a bend to cool. It's one of the easiest ways to increase productivity without increasing nervous strain.

6) "T" or "Y" connector.
Use a "T" or "Y" connector on a pumping manifold to process two or more units at a time. By pumping multiple units, you'll spend less time at the bombarder and more time blowing glass, selling or installing signs. Naturally, this assumes your tube processing equipment is suitable to the task. If not, consider upgrading for this benefit.

5) Proper lighting.
Being in the business of shaping light, one would think that we all work under the best possible lighting. But in many shops, this just is not the case.

Too much direct light glares off the tube making it difficult to judge its position in the flame. Even offset direct light can make the flame unseeable and thus impossible to position the tube properly.

Insufficient light or lighting that causes too many shadows is a problem too; it makes the pattern tricky to see. How do you match molten glass to a pattern you can't perceive?

So, consider using neon as a light source - its inventor's original intent. Neon border tubes, signs or art pieces mounted around the shop offer diffuse, colorful light and add mood and reduce shadows.

4) Bending table datum.
Datum, who chose that word? But that's right folks, size does matter. The bending table's dimensions and even position in the shop makes a big difference in both comfort and productivity.

Constructing a worktable the suitable height reduces potential back, shoulder and leg strain. And adjusting it is as simple as cutting down the length of a table's legs or blocking them up.

If the craftsman is much shorter than the table or the legs cannot further be trimmed, build a platform for the craftsman to stand on. Then while you're at it, run under the platform all hoses connecting to the burners. This effectively clears the workspace.

Build a large table for manufacturing channel letters and border tubes, five or six feet deep by ten or twelve feet long. If you like, construct a smaller surface for manufacturing window signs. But the extra space is always welcome particularly when mass-producing signs. Finally, add a layer of heat resistant sheetrock to help cool the molten glass evenly then cover all with heat resistant, non-asbestos fabric.

Properly positioning the table in the shop helps avoid slow downs and safety hazards. Busy pathways are a distraction for the craftsman and open flame and molten glass a danger to passerby. So, position the table out of the way but not such that typical movements are restricted by low ceilings or otherwise protruding obstructions.

Consider additions to the table like an attached cooling rack and yard stick. A cooling rack provides a safe place for hot bends to evenly cool strengthening the glasswork. It also clears the space so other work may continue. A yardstick attached to the table makes for quick calculation and tube marking.

3) Anti fatigue mats.

Buy good ones, say, one and one-half inch to a full inch thick. Most sign shop floors are concrete. Standing on concrete all day unnecessarily tasks feet, legs and back. Providing good anti fatigue mats is one of the cheapest, easiest and best ways to increase productivity and maintain employee happiness and health.

Use a good electrical insulating mat in front of the bombarding station. This offers comfort and lessens chance of minor shock from a sparkcoil or even electrocution during bombarding.

2) Proper ventilation and air conditioning.
Neon shop burners consume oxygen and give off small amounts of gases and airborne particles. Regular replacement of shop air is not only wise it's required by air quality agencies. So, make certain you use some system of ventilation. Have the air quality checked by a proper agency if you're in doubt.

Molten neon tubing is around twelve hundred degrees Fahrenheit in temperature. Slap that onto a wood table and although its surface is protected with non-asbestos covering, you'll still see and smell smoke. Breathing only fumes from scorched insulating material and a smoldering tabletop is not only unhealthy; it's unnecessary. Proper ventilation is important.

And finally, working over the top of a blue flame is only comfortable in the dead of winter. Air conditioning doesn't just add comfort it also increases productiveness. Ever witness what happens to molten glass when a bead of sweat strikes it? It's an unsafe and shattering experience.

1) Properly operating burners.
Properly operating burners are crucial to productivity. A cool flame slows work and increases chance for strain developing in both a glass bend and glassblower. And a burner that produces a rich flame causes the glass to "smoke" as the metal lead is chemically removed from the glass mixture and deposited on the tube surface. This weakens the bend and is unsightly too.

Position well-operating burners away but not far from the bending table. Well-placed burners allow sufficient room for maneuvering the tube during heating. It also allows room to move while matching the bend to a pattern. Little is more frustrating than running the tube into a burner while attempting to form that perfect bend.

Well, I hope you agree with at least some of my favorite Top 10 Must-Haves. But more importantly, I hope you have already incorporated them into your shop.

Q&A

Q) How can I locate a leak in my manifold? Can I use a spark coil?

A) You can use a spark coil to locate a leak. So long as it's on a lead glass manifold with greasable stopcocks. And so long as you keep the spark a safe distance from the stopcocks (though I've seen them tested with a coil too). But spark coil use is not recommended on a Pyrex manifold with so-called greaseless stopcocks as it can damage the o-ring seals. Whenever you use a spark coil, keep the spark setting low.

However, first consider regreasing all the stopcocks or replacing the o-rings if your manifold uses greaseless stopcocks. The sneakiest of leaks usually presents itself here and it's less bother and potential trouble than digging for a leak in the manifold body.

Otherwise, a rather simple leak finding method is to spray the manifold with soapy water, stopcocks too, while blowing hard into it. A leak will show as tiny, intermittent bubbles unless the leak is exceptionally small. Pay particular attention to old welds and stopcocks.

If the manifold is made of greaseless connector sections, remove the outermost section and seal the remainder. Then evacuate and test to see if the leak persists. Repeat this until you find the section at fault.

Even inert gas containers can leak into the manifold. If your blue, argon units show a tint of red after gassing, the neon flask stopcock may be at fault. Or if your neon units glow with a purple haze, consider checking the argon container seals.

Now, if the leak still doesn't show itself, pull loose the vacuum hose from the pump, clean, grease and refit it or even replace it. Sometimes a leak isn't in the manifold at all.

Q) My ribbon burner sometimes produces an orange flame and doesn't melt glass well. What causes this?

A) Intermittent, discolored flames often are indicative of vapors or particles entering the blower. If your blower is in or near a paint or other work room, it's possible vapors or other matter are entering from there. Some vapors are dangerous when heated so, if this is true consider moving the blower to a safer location.

But because you specified the flame color as orange, I'll bet your blower is mounted outdoors or near an open exit. During driving rain, water vapor mixes with air, is drawn into the blower then pushed to the burner. As when bombarding a tube, the moisture emits the color orange when heated. Excess moisture in a flame alters its properties and makes melting glass almost impossible. So, again the solution is to move the blower this time to a drier location.

Q) Why use argon instead of neon to make blue tubes? Doesn't mercury turn a neon filled tube blue too?

A) Yes, adding mercury to a neon filled tube will turn it as blue as an argon filled tube. But one reason argon is used instead of neon is that argon is a better carrier or transport for mercury vapor.

And because argon is made of a larger atom than neon, it requires less electrical energy to light; we can light more tubes on a given transformer. In cold weather, when mercury tends to return to a liquid state, an argon tube simply dims; it doesn't change color, which might really upset a sign owner.

Some neon artists use a balance of mercury vapor in their neon filled tubes to add color-changing effects. In clear glass tubes, obviously the color red mixes with blue. But coated tubes alternate between their designated argon/mercury and neon colors like turquoise and peach, green and amber, etceteras. Pretty cool.

Q) I know light in argon tubes sometimes wiggles or snakes. Is this because the tube wasn't properly processed?

A) Snaking or wriggling is caused when at least two gaseous components remain in the tube; one heavier than the inert gas and one lighter. These added components are considered impurities in a conventional neon tube however; neon artists often work to create this effect.

Improper tube processing often leads to snaking, overheating of the electrodes, inadequate pumping or insufficient warming of the tube. Other causes include: using an excessively dirty tube, one that's laid in the open a considerable time and introducing impure mercury that contributes to the admixture.

There's no way to completely control all the factors that cause snaking. But following a few fundamental rules will help minimize those factors: store glass in a clean, sealed container or cork the tube ends; minimize the introduction of other contaminants by using a clean blowhose and connector set; use premium electrodes and glass; process immediately finished units and follow religiously the electrode manufacturer's method of tube and electrode processing.

Q) How fast can a journeyman glassblower work? How fast is fast?

A) How fast a glassblower produces a marketable product is the sum of many factors, not only skill. The type and size of glass used matters a lot. Classic glass and large diameter tubes often take longer to heat and so can slow the work. Some designs complicate matters and may hamper productivity. Even something as obscure as poor lighting, inadequate ventilation or the onset of the common cold can affect a craftsman and their production speed.

I calculate my own productivity by counting the number of minutes per bend I average on a given project. Typically, when working on a custom job the first time through, I'm pleased if I average three minutes per bend. During an eight-hour day, that works out to one hundred sixty bends or about eight typical OPEN signs.

On a real good day when working on a mass produced product, I'm happy when I average one to one and a half minutes per bend. That equals between four hundred eighty and three hundred twenty bends per day or equivalently between twenty-four and sixteen OPENs a day.

On a real bad day, I'm happy if I don't destroy work from the day before. In this field dominated by Murphy's Law, working backward is within the realm of possibility.

Q) I leave my butyl U-gauge closed when not in use to detect minute leaks in my system. I know when the butyl oil climbs on the stopcock side that I have a system leak. But sometimes the butyl oil climbs on the opposite side of the gauge! What causes this?

A) This butyl U-gauge likely uses a grease-sealing type stopcock, though I have seen this phenomenon with greaseless stopcocks too. If this is a greaseless stopcock, replacing the o-ring should fix the problem. If this is a grease type stopcock consider the following:

Normally, air leaking into a manifold cannot get past a closed butyl U-gauge stopcock. So, it exerts force on the butyl oil column opposite the stopcock causing the fluid to climb on the stopcock side.

But when air finds its way past the butyl gauge stopcock, a force is exerted on that side of the butyl oil column and causes the fluid to climb opposite the stopcock. This makes it difficult to neutralize the butyl gauge to make repairs; you have to juggle neutralizing the manifold and easing out the butyl gauge stopcock allowing the air pressure to slowly balance.

The long-term solution is to clean the stopcock then apply a new film of grease. If the problem persists, it may be necessary to replace the stopcock with a new one.

Q) I'm not a tubebender but one of my jobs is to help run our wholesale neon shop. Some customers provide paper patterns and others fabric. Is one way better than another? What are the pros and cons?

A) Since you manage a wholesale shop, I imagine speed or volume production is important. I have a couple tips, I think your tubebenders will appreciate.

Patterns drawn on fabric are desirable when bending small letters, say under four inches tall. That's because small diameter tubes, ten-millimeter or less, are often used to form them.

Metal screen laid over a paper pattern seldom lies perfectly flat and so sometimes distorts a small tube bend beyond usefulness. Large diameter tubes are heavier and less susceptible to trouble caused by screen distortions.

So, anytime a pattern calls for multiple units made in a tube diameter ten-millimeter or less, consider requesting the pattern be on fabric or transfer it yourself.

Also, consider darkening pattern lines on paper patterns. Too often, the patterns are drawn in light pencil. When a glassblower lays a screen over the paper, the pattern nearly disappears from view potentially slowing production.

If you get your customers to follow these suggestions and provide you with proper patterns, you'll likely increase production and provide the customer a better product in record time.

Q) How do they figure the numbers on white tubes, 3500, 4500, 6500, etcetera? I know the tubes with higher numbers are whiter.

A) The numbers listed on white tubes indicate temperature in degrees Kelvin. The Kelvin temperature scale is one that begins at absolute zero or -273.16 degrees Celsius, -459.69 degrees Fahrenheit. Very cold indeed.

The freezing point of water, 32 degrees Fahrenheit, is 273.00 degrees Kelvin. The boiling point of water, 212 degrees Fahrenheit is 373.00 Kelvin. Confused yet?

A neon tube manufacturer labels a white neon tube according to the color match or light wavelength between the lit white tube and the heated metal, I believe to be Tungsten.

For instance, when the metal is heated to 3500 degrees Kelvin, it glows yellow-white like a 3500 white tube. Heated to 6500 degrees Kelvin, Tungsten glows almost blue-white, hence the labeling of a 6500 white tube and so on.

Mercury In The Shop

Mercury or quicksilver as it is called, is that shiny, silver-white, odorless liquid we neon craftsman innocently roll into argon filled tubes to brighten them. We also use it in some diffusion pumps attached to our tube pumping system to aid tube processing. But did you know mercury is everywhere?

Mercury Everywhere

Mercury is used in thermometers, mercury-vapor lamps, dental fillings, batteries, scientific and electrical equipment, medicinally as "Mercurochrome" and in the production of some chemicals, even to produce polyurethane foam. It's in the atmosphere, the soil, in our streams and oceans, in animals, and our bodies too.

It enters the air from manufacturing plants, mining operations and from burning coal and waste. It directly enters the soil and water from the use of some fungicides, the disposal of certain wastes and from natural deposits too.

It rests on our workbenches, rolls onto our floors, sits in our manifolds and spills into the shop walls. And mercury-filled, argon tubes dump it into our neighborhoods too. So since it's everywhere, let's try to understand this surreptitious little inhabitant, mercury, a little better.

Some Facts

Mercury was first separated as an element by French chemist Antoine Laurent Lavoisier. In nature, it generally occurs in compounds combined in the form of sulfides. It's found in its most pure form with the metal silver and ranks about 67th in abundance among the elements with cinnebar ore producing the most mercury.

Toxicity, Exposure And Risks

We've all heard that mercury is dangerous to our health, that its careful use and disposal is not only required, it is mandated. But how many of us heed those warnings? Are these warnings even appropriate? Really, just how dangerous is mercury?

Mercury's toxicity depends on its chemical state; some forms are even considered non-hazardous. The most toxic forms are methylmercury compounds. Dimethyl mercury is strong smelling and boils at 205 degrees Fahrenheit. It is considered one of the most poisonous substances known to man and can be inhaled or absorbed through the skin. Methylmercury is also the form that builds up in the tissues of fish and other organisms. Its levels generally increase as we move up the food chain.

As a vapor, mercury is extremely dangerous. Allowed to stand open in a poorly ventilated room for long periods, it can affect people regularly occupying that room. Its one reason adequate ventilation is so very important in a neon shop.

Though mercury vaporizes little at room temperature those vapors are readily absorbed into the lungs and distributed by the circulatory system. Some mercury remains in the brain but most is carried to the liver and kidneys where it is laboriously eliminated through bile and urine. Signs of exposure are usually separated into two categories, Acute and Chronic.

Acute exposure may cause chills, nausea, mild sickness or depression, tightness in the chest or chest pains, labored respiration, cough, inflammation of the mouth, inflammation of the gums, salivation, and diarrhea.

Chronic exposure may cause weakness, prolonged eating disorder, weight loss, and other digestive problems. A tremor beginning in the fingers, eyelids, and lips can spread to the entire body. Behavioral changes include excitability, memory loss, sleeplessness, and depression.

Other chronic symptoms include rashes, excessive sweating, severe salivation, fever, and painful peeling of the skin on the hands and feet. Long-term damage to the kidneys, the immune and/or nervous system even death can result from chronic exposure.

Ingested mercury is not safe either. Small amounts repeatedly ingested over long periods of time can cause irreversible brain, liver and kidney damage even unwanted reproductive effects.

Limiting Exposure
Mercury vapor is colorless and odorless; you won't see or smell it coming. So, adequate ventilation is the simplest precaution against long term exposure.

The Occupational Safety and Health Administration (OSHA) determines a worker's exposure to airborne mercury vapor by collecting air samples and analyzing them. Their ceiling limit of permissible exposure is 0.1 milligram per cubic meter of air. The National Institute sets exposure limit per workday and workweek for Occupational Safety and Health.

Proper mercury handling is your next best precaution. Make certain all mercury containers are well sealed and that all spills are collected using an acceptable mercury collection system.

Check with your local sign supply distributor or local scientific equipment supply house to locate mercury spill cleanup kits. These systems vary widely in price and application so shop around.

A simple sponge is designed for micro-droplet cleanup and can cost well under fifty dollars. A powder that absorbs larger droplets and changes color in the presence of mercury usually costs less than forty dollars. But an industrial size emergency cleanup kit that can clean up several liters of mercury will cost as much as five hundred dollars and is likely overkill for use in a typical neon shop.

Medical Surveillance
Currently, OSHA is developing medical surveillance and procedure guidelines. They will be used to determine whether employees exposed to mercury vapor are required to utilize the following and other medical procedures.

Preplacement medical evaluations would consider the potential for mercury vapor exposure and document initial baseline, health status. Systematic follow-up healthcare interviews and tests would help to prevent occupational injury and disease.

The program may include mandated Federal, State or local standards or where none exist, recommend evaluations every three to five years. Tests of urine and blood may be included to determine biological exposure. Doctors may also test scalp hair to measure exposure to methylmercury.

Reporting Spills
OSHA states, "Reportable quantity requirements for hazardous releases. A hazardous substance release is defined by EPA as any spilling, leaking, pumping, pouring, emitting, emptying, discharging, injecting, escaping, leaching, dumping, or disposing into the environment (including the abandonment or discarding of contaminated containers) of hazardous substances. In the event of a release that is above the reportable quantity for that chemical, employers are required to notify the proper Federal, State, and local authorities [40 CFR 355.40]."

Now, they also state, "The reportable quantity of mercury is 1 pound. If an amount equal to or greater than this quantity is released within a 24-hour period in a manner that will expose persons outside the facility, employers are required to do the following: - Notify the National Response Center immediately at (800) 424-8802 or at (202) 426-2675 in Washington, D.C. [40 CFR 302.6]."

This means that the typical, small mercury spill contained in a neon shop does not require reporting to the National Response Center. However, as I have witnessed, some sign shop personnel actually dump bottles of dirty mercury into storm sewer drains. This is not acceptable! It pollutes our waterways and sea animals and works its way up the food chain into people. It may also invite unwanted regulation and enforcement. So, what to do?

A Better Solution On the Horizon?
A new product may provide the answer. It's called, Quicksilver - The Neon Electrode With Mercury Built-In is manufactured by Masonlite, Ltd., 36 second Avenue, Chatham, Kent ME4 5AX or in the United States, Masonlite, Ltd., 35 Lumber Road, Roslyn, NY 11578.

Glossary of Terms

Aging or burning-in: The electrochemical stabilization of a neon unit performed after tube processing by wiring the unit to a suitable transformer until proper color develops.

Air blower or air supply: A mechanical air pump capable of supplying a constant, steady flow of low pressure, high volume air to burners.

Annealing: The controlled, slow cooling of glass from molten state to strain point in order to minimize glass strains. See Table Annealing.

Argon: An inert gas used with mercury to create blue light in neon tubes. Argon is dim lavender when ionized alone.

Atmospheric pressure: The pressure created by the weight of the atmosphere at sea level, about 14.7 pounds per square inch or 760 millimeters of mercury.

Blockout or opaquing: A way to conceal visible lengths of lit tubing or electrodes with special light blocking paint. See Dip Tank.

Blowhose: A flexible latex or rubber tube connecting a mouthpiece on one end and a tube connector set on the other. The glassblower displaces air through the blowhose to expand or contract the diameter of molten tubing.

Bombarding: Tube processing, purifying the inside of a tube with electricity. Electricity is used to burn or vaporize impurities readying them for removal by the vacuum pump. Also see Tube Processing.

Border tube: Lit tubes, usually straight, that run along the perimeter of a window, room or architectural line forming a border of light.

Borosilicate: Hard glass used to make manifolds, seldom used to manufacture neon signs.

Butyl oil, butyl phthalate: An organic liquid used in butyl or U-gauges to indicate inert gas filling pressures.

Celsius or Centigrade: A temperature scale defining zero degrees as the freezing point of water and one hundred degrees as the boiling point: $°C=(°F-32)(5/9)$.

<u>Channel Letter:</u> Usually neon lit, cut-to-shape acrylic faced letters. The neon tube resides in or behind a can or pan made of sheet metal or plastic.

<u>Classic glass:</u> Color impregnated soda glass tubing. Usually difficult to bend and expensive.

<u>Claude, Georges:</u> Considered the father of the neon industry and known as Claude Neon, this Frenchman worked to promote neon, both technically and commercially, by developing and patenting the first long-life electrode.

<u>Coated tubing:</u> Neon tubing with phosphors adhered evenly to the inside wall. The phosphors absorb light given off by an inert gas and emit light of a different color.

<u>Coefficient of expansion of glass tubing:</u> A numerical value determined by the elongation of glass tubing per degree of temperature change. Two greatly dissimilar expansion rates means the tubes will not seal together.

<u>Cork:</u> A stopper used to seal a glass tube end usually made of cork material.

<u>Crossfire:</u> A burner consisting of several individual finger torches that are divided equally between two heads and aim at a common focal point.

<u>Current:</u> The flow of charged particles frequently measured in amperes or milliamperes.

<u>Diffusion pump:</u> Made of glass or metal, these pumps employ the principles of expanding and condensing hot, low vapor pressure liquids to increase both the degree and speed of vacuuming a tube.

<u>Dip Tank:</u> A metal can filled with blockout paint. Dipping the back of a finished neon unit into the dip tank speeds the tube painting procedure.

<u>Drop or Raise:</u> A bend defined as a change of elevation and direction. Ordinarily, the tube elevation is changed one block height and the direction 90 degrees.

<u>Dumet wire or lead:</u> A copper sheathed wire having the same coefficient of expansion as lead glass. It is the copper colored wire found at the pinch seal of an electrode.

<u>Electrode:</u> An electrical current carrying device designed to transfer electrical energy to inert gas. Made of a metal shell surrounded by glass, electrodes are attached to the ends of a neon unit.

Electron: A subatomic, negatively charged particle that orbits the atomic nucleus or travels freely with the flow of electricity. When an electron drops to a lower energy state within the atom of an inert gas, it emits a photon.

Emission (emitter) coating: Refers to the chemical coating, mostly barium hydroxide and calcium and strontium carbonates, applied to the electrode shell to protect it from sputter during bombarding. Failure to convert the coating releases impurities into a tube causing discoloration and possibly mercury stains.

Fahrenheit: A temperature scale where the freezing point of water is 32 degrees and the boiling point of water is 212 degrees. ºF=(9/5ºC)+32. See Celsius or Centigrade.

Flask: A thin necked, globular glass container that holds gases used to flush or fill neon units. New flasks are filled to atmospheric pressure.

Gas: The molecular state of air like substances as opposed to the two other physical states of matter, liquid and solid.

GTO: Refers to high voltage or high tension insulated wire used to connect electrode to transformer or electrode to electrode.

Helium: Another inert gas that lights orange-white. Seldom used in neon.

Housing: A glass or ceramic protective covering for an electrode.

Impurity: Refers to unwanted contaminants within a finished tube.

Ion: An atom carrying a positive or negative charge depending on lost or gained electrons.

Kilovolt-ampere (Kva): An electrical measurement of power equal to 1000 volt-amperes. A bombarding transformer rating found by multiplying the primary voltage and current, then dividing the product by 1000. Common bombarding transformer ratings are 5 Kva to 15 Kva.

Krypton: An inert gas found in the atmosphere at about one part per million. It ionizes somewhat dim silvery-lavender in color.

L-bend: A 90 degree change of direction of tubing.

Lead-alkali glass: Referring to the common glass tube used in the neon trade. A glass composite made of mostly silicon dioxide and a form of lead oxide. Invented by George Ravenscroft, a British chemist, in 1676.

Lead-in wire: The wire extending from an electrode that connects the electrode shell to a transformer lead. Usually a stranded three-piece wire.

Legibility: Referring to ease at which a letter is read. Dealing with letter size, style, color, background, etcetera.

Letter style (typeface): Differing types and sizes of letters. For example, a form of script or block, serif or sans serif, in bold, italic, or extended, etcetera.

Listing agency: A testing and quality control agency that inspects sign company electrical products for accepted materials use and assembly methods for a fee. Common services include E.T.L. (Electrical Testing Laboratories), U.L. (Underwriter's Laboratories, Inc.) and C.S.A. (Canadian Standards Association).

Luminous tube: Referring to neon: a sealed vacuum tube that uses electrodes to transfer electrical energy to pure inert gases within a tube to produce light.

Mapping a pattern: Determining which bend would best represent the design and indicating that bend on the pattern.

Map measuring wheel: A measuring device used to determine from a pattern the linear footage of tubing needed in a unit or sign.

Mercury or Quick Silver: A silvery metal element that is liquid at room temperature. It is used to brighten argon tubes to commercially viable levels. Used to create blue gas. When heated to high temperatures, mercury vapors are extremely toxic.

Mercury trap: A hand blown glass orb that holds mercury away from the unit during bombarding and burn-in.

Mercury tube: A tube filled with argon and mercury to make blue gas.

Mica: A thin sheet of semitransparent mineral silicate used to electrically insulate close tubes during bombarding. This helps avoid electricity shorting through the glass bends, also known as blow through.

Micron: 1/1000 of a millimeter. 1/1000 of a Torr. 1/25,400 of an inch. A measurement of high vacuums. Numerically equivalent to milli-Torr.

Milliammeter: An instrument to measure electric current in milliamperes.

Milliampere: 1/1000 of an ampere. A measure of electric current

Millimeter of mercury: The height of a column of mercury supported against gravity by the pressure of a gas or gases. The atmosphere supports a column of mercury about 760 millimeters high. Used to measure relative vacuum, the numerical equivalent to Torr.

Neon: A colorless, tasteless, odorless, inert gas found in small quantities in the atmosphere. Neon gas glows red-orange when illuminated. Also used in reference to a luminous tube manufactured by a neon glassblower, a neon tube or neon unit.

Nitrogen: A colorless, tasteless, odorless gaseous element making up about 78% of the atmosphere. It is considered an impurity in a neon tube.

Offset: A bend causing a change of elevation and direction of tubing. The elevation change is ordinarily one block height and the direction less than 90 degrees.

Outdoor neon: Tubes manufactured for outdoor use. Argon mercury tubes are often filled with a mixture of neon and argon, 20%-80% or 40%-60% respectively, to run the tube warmer. This helps maintain even brightness throughout a mercury filled tube even in cold weather.

Outgas: Refers to a liquid or solid vaporizing under vacuum or heat.

Oxygen: A colorless, tasteless, odorless gas element making up about 21% of the atmosphere. It is considered an impurity in a completed neon tube.

Pattern: A reversed layout to form a neon tube to.

Penetration: A length of tube with electrode designed to penetrate a structure a given length to facilitate installation.

Phosphors: Chemical coatings adhered inside coated tubes. They absorb light emitted by the fill gas then emit light of another color.

Pirani gauge: A gauge used to indicate high vacuum, low relative pressure.

Pumping system: Refers to a manifold, vacuum pump and other vacuum peripherals used to evacuate a tube during tube processing.

Rare, noble, or inert gases: Refers to the inactive gases found in the far right column of the Periodic Table of the Elements.

Ribbon burner: A burner with an adjustable length flame used to form long curves and script style lettering. Most common is the 16 inch burner but 6 and 24 inch burners are also available.

Silicon dioxide: The chemical name for the major constituent of most types of glass. Also called silica.

Silicone fluids: Refers to silicone based fluids used in some diffusion pumps.

Skeleton sign: Refers to a neon window sign using a glass tube frame. The sign is suspended from the tube frame.

Snaking (wriggling): A phenomenon nearly exclusive to argon filled tubes. It is identifiable by a swaying beam of light. Insufficient tube processing can result in snaking. It is caused when at least two impurities remain in a finished tube. One impurity is heavier than the inert fill gas and the other is lighter–usually carbon monoxide or carbon dioxide and hydrogen. By virtue of molecular mass, the two impurities constantly displace inert gas molecules. Choosing a path of least resistance, the electric current follows the path set by the inert gas causing the beam of light to *snake* through the tube, sometimes splitting into two or more beams.

Soda-lime glass: A glass with similar expansion coefficient as that of lead glass. Its main constituents are silicon dioxide and soda-lime. Tubes composed of soda-lime glass and metal oxides produce rich colors. They are called classic or exotic glass tubes and are more expensive and difficult to work than lead glass tubes.

Spark coil: A high voltage, high frequency Tesla coil capable of throwing a ground seeking spark about one inch long. Commonly used to locate leaks in a tube.

Splicing glass: The act of joining two tubes by heat, welding.

Sputtering: The destruction of an electrode shell by ionic bombardment. Usually caused from excessive current and/or vacuum during bombarding resulting in premature emitter coating processing. Also caused over time by improper inert gas fill pressure.

Stopcock: A high vacuum valve used to control various functions on a manifold. Stopcocks are made of lead or borosilicate glass or metal.

Strain: Destructive forces caused within a tube glass wall due to improper heating, handling or cooling. Strains often lead to cracks, splits or breaks in the glass.

Supports (standoffs): Tube supporting insulators made varying lengths that keep the neon tube away from another material. They usually are made of acrylic, glass or metal. Some standoffs are spring loaded to absorb shock during shipping.

Swivel: A brass pivoting device attached to a blowhose and connector that allows tube rotation without twisting or knotting the blowhose.

Table annealing: Though not true annealing, table annealing refers to cooling a bend or weld before moving for 30 seconds or more. This allows most tubes time to cool beyond the strain point and reduces or eliminates strain in the glass. Large diameter tubes cool slower, by virtue of greater mass, and need to cool longer.

Test coil: See Spark coil.

Tie wire: Copper wire used to tie neon tubes to supports.

Torch: Refers to the many types of burners used to accomplish a glass working task: crossfire, cannon fire, ribbon fire and handtorch.

Torr: A unit of pressure relating to vacuum, the equivalent numerical measure to millimeter of mercury. See millimeter of mercury.

Transformer: An electrical device used to power neon tubes. Neon tubes use *step-up* transformers to increase low wall voltage to high voltage. Transformer styles include: indoor and outdoor models; window and window compact versions; solid state and core-n-coil; midpoint ground and bombarding.

Transition point: The point between one ribbon curve and the next where previously heated tubing heats more slowly than unheated tubing.

Tube processing: The internal purification and filling of a finished glass tube. Usually includes bombarding, pumping and filling with inert gas.

Tube supports: see supports.

Tubulated electrode: An electrode manufactured with a length of small, often five millimeter tubing, projecting from the pinch seal. Tubes are pumped and filled through the tubulation.

Tubulating: Blowing a small hole in the side of a tube, usually near the unit center, then sealing a short length of five millimeter tubing to the hole. This provides a pathway to evacuate and fill a tube.

U-bend: A bend that changes tube direction 180 degrees. Also called a Doubleback when formed as a three dimensional bend.

U-gauge: A butyl gauge or manometer used to measure fill gas pressure.

Ultraviolet light: Light higher in frequency than the color violet, invisible to the human eye. Nearly all ultraviolet light is absorbed by the lead glass wall before it leaves the tube. Phosphor coatings absorb ultraviolet light and emit it at a different wave length changing the tube color.

Unit: Refers to a neon tube section complete with electrodes. A sign may consist of one or many units.

Vacuum: Refers to any pressure less than reference pressure. When a unit is evacuated, it is under vacuum compared to atmospheric pressure.

Vacuum gauge: A mechanical or electrical gauge used to indicate relative vacuum in a tube.

Vapor: A substance in a gaseous state as opposed to a liquid or solid state.

V-bend: A sharp change of tube direction between 90 and 180 degrees.

Visibility: The ability to be seen. Not necessarily legible, but visible.

Voltage: An electrical potential difference; the *push* of electricity.

Window sign: A sign designed to hang in a window as opposed to being mounted on a wall, facia or pole.

Xenon: A colorless inert gaseous element making up about one part in 20 million in the atmosphere. It lights a unique silver-blue-white glow.

Index

A

B

C

D

E

F

G

H

I

J

K

L

M

N

O

P

R

S

W

X

Resources

Aries Graphics International Neon Wizard
365 S. Rancho Santa Fe Rd., Suite 202
San Marcos, CA 92069 USA
Phone: 760.752.7640
Fax: 760.752.3221
Email: sales@aries-graphics.com
Website: www.aries-graphics.com

DACO Neon Equipment
POB 461084
Papillion, NE 68046 USA
Phone: 402.331.2164
Fax: 402.331.8259
Email: daco@daconeon.com
Website: www.daconeon.com

Edwards High Vacuum International
301 Ballardvale St.
Wilmington, MA 01887 USA
Phone: 800.848.9800
Fax: 508.658.7969
Website: www.boc.com/evt

Eric Ehlenberger - Neon Artist
724 Foucher
New Orleans, LA 70115
Phone: 504.891.4865
Fax: 504.269.4226
Email: eric@neonSculpture.com

GlassLight Gallery:
728 St. Louis St.
New Orleans, LA 70130
Phone: 504.587.7051
Email: gallery@neonSculpture.com
Websites:
GlassLight Gallery: http://www.neonSculpture.com
Complete works: www.Ehlenberger.com
Electroluminescent sculpture: www.ELsculpture.com
Neon clocks: www.neon-clock.com

Haley Ryane (certified instructor)
Savage Neon, Inc.
4900 Wetheredsville Road
Baltimore, MD 21207
Phone: 410-448-5483
Fax: 410-448-5490
Toll-free: 800-465-8001
Email: neonsavage@juno.com
Website: www.savageneon.com

Mike Wheeler
Custom Glassblowing
431 North Jesse Street
Chandler, AZ 85225
Phone: 480.786.4323 voice and fax
Email: wheelerglass@inficad.com
Website: www.inficad.com/~wheelerglass

Sign Builder Illustrated Magazine
Williamsburg Common
323 Clifton Street, Suite #7
Greenville, NC 27858
Phone: 252.355.5806
Fax: 252.355.5690
Email: jeff@signshop.com
Website: www.signshop.com

SPI
569 East Gay Street, West Chester, PA 19380
Phone: 610.436.5400
Fax: 610.436.5755
Email: spi3spi@2spi.com
Website: www.2spi.com

Transco, Inc.
1059 Colite Drive
West Columbia, SC. 29170
Phone: 800.869.6366
Fax: 803.794.8528
Email: transco@earthlink.net
Website: www.transco-neon.com